THE MAN UTD
QUIZ BOOK

600 Fun Questions for

Manchester United Fans Everywhere

JAMES CONRAD

James Conrad has asserted his moral right to be identified as the author of this work in accordance with the Copyright, Designs and Patents Act 1988.

Published by MP Publishing
Copyright © 2020

CONTENTS

INTRODUCTION

At Manchester United we strive for perfection and if we fail, we may just have to settle for excellence.

Sir Matt Busby

This book has six hundred questions for dedicated Manchester United fans wherever you are. The questions are about its history, its achievements, its players, its managers and many other things United.

The questions are generally in a multiple-choice format and are of varying degrees of difficulty to test the knowledge of all fans.

The Manchester United Quiz Book is both entertaining and informative and will provide hours of memory wracking entertainment for Manchester fans.

QUIZ 1: THE START

1.What year was Manchester United founded?
   a) 1878 b) 1882 c) 1886

2.What was the first name of the club?
   a) Manchester Eagles b) Trafford FC c) Newton Heath LYR FC

3. What were their first kit colours?
   a) Green and gold   b) Green and white   c) Yellow and red

4. In which competition did they play their first competitive game?
   a) The Combination League   b) Football Alliance c) FA Cup

5. In what year did they change their name to Manchester United?
   a) 1899   b) 1902   c) 1910

6. When did they reach their lowest ever league position?
   a) 1922 – 23   b) 1928 – 29   c) 1933 – 34

7. In what year did they enter the Football League?
   a) 1892 – 93   b) 1897 -98   c) 1900 – 01

8.Where did they finish in the league in their first season?
   a) First   b) Sixth   c) Twentieth

9.When did Man Utd move to Old Trafford?
   a) 1908   b) 1910   c) 1912

10. Who were their opponents in their first game at Old Trafford?
   a) Liverpool b) Man City c) Bury

Quiz 2: Sir Alex Ferguson

1. What is Alex Ferguson's middle name?
   a) Gordon b) Dundas c) Chapman

2. Which club was his first managerial appointment?
   a) Aberdeen b) East Stirlingshire c) St Mirren

3. How many league titles did Sir Alex win as manager of Aberdeen?
   a) 2   b) 3   c) 4

4. What year was he appointed manager of Man Utd?
   a) 1986 b) 1987   c) 1988

5. How many times did Man Utd win the Premier League under Sir Alex?
   a) 12   b) 13   c) 14

6. Who was the manager of Man Utd prior to Sir Alex's arrival?
   a) Matt Busby b) Tommy Docherty c) Ron Atkinson

7. Who were the first league opponents that Sir Alex faced as Man Utd manager?
   a) Reading b) Barnsley c) Oxford United

8. What was the score in his final game in charge of Man Utd against West Brom?
   a) 2 – 1 b) 3 – 2 c) 5 – 5

9. What year did Sir Alex retire as manager of Man Utd?
   a) 2011 b) 2012 c) 2013

10. How many FA Cups did Sir Alex win with Man Utd?
    a) 4 b) 5 c) 6

Quiz 3: Sir Matt Busby

1. **What year was Matt Busby born in?**
   a) 1905 b) 1907 c) 1909

2. **What is his first name?**
   a) Sinclair b) Ferguson c) Alexander

3. **What was his first full time job?**
   a) Boot cleaner b) Collier c) Grounds man

4. **What was the first English team he played for?**
   a) Man Utd b) Man City c) Liverpool

5. **How many times did he play for Scotland?**
   a) 1 b) 12 c) 28

6. **Which year did Sir Matt take over as Man Utd manager?**
   a) 1945 b) 1947 c) 1949

7. **Which team did Matt Busby manage between July 1948 and August 1948?**
   a) England b) Scotland c) Great Britain

8. **Which Spanish job was he offered in 1956?**
   a) Barcelona b) Seville c) Real Madrid

9. **How many First Division titles did Matt Busby win at Man Utd?**
   a) 3 b) 4 c) 5

10. **How many FA Cups did Matt Busby win in his career?**
    a) 2 b) 3 c) 4

Quiz 4: Jose Mourinho

1. Which country was Mourinho born in?
   a) Spain b) Italy c) Portugal

2. In 2000 Mourinho took the job at Sporting CP as interpreter/coach to which manager?
   a) George Graham b) Bobby Robson c) Graham Taylor

3. What was the first team he managed?
   a) Porto b) Benfica c) Inter Milan

4. Who did Mourinho take over from as manager of Man Utd?
   a) Van Gaal b) Giggs c) Moyes

5. How many trophies did he win with Man Utd?
   a) 1 b) 2 c) 3

6. Mourinho has won the Champions League twice with which teams?
   a) Real Madrid and Porto b) Inter Milan and Real Madrid c) Inter Milan and Porto

7. In the 2017 – 18 season which Spanish team knocked Mourinho's Man Utd out of the Champions League at the last 16 stage?
   a) Valencia b) Sevilla c) Ath Bilbao

8. In the 2017 – 18 season where did Man Utd finish in the table?
   a) 2nd b) 3rd c) 4th

9. Man Utd lost the 2018 FA Cup Final to which team?
   a) Arsenal b) Tottenham c) Chelsea

10. Mourinho was sacked by Man Utd on 18th December 2018. Who were his last opponents as manager?

    a)   Liverpool b) Man City c) Bournemouth

Quiz 5: David Moyes

1. Where was David Moyes born?

    a)   Dunfermline b) Aberdeen c) Glasgow

2. What was the first senior team that he played for?

    a)   Ayr b) Dundee United c) Celtic

3. Where did Moyes begin his management career?

    a)   Everton b) Bury c) Preston North End

4. Who did he take over from as manager of Everton?

    a)   Walter Smith b) Howard Kendall c) Dave Watson

5. How long was the contract that David Moyes signed with Man Utd?

    a)   2 years b) 4 years c) 6 years

6. How long was he in charge of Man Utd?

    a)   10 months b) 13 months c) 15 months

7. What was the only trophy he won as manager of Man Utd?

    a)   FA Cup 2013 b) Community Shield 2013 c) Europa League 2013

8. Who did they beat to win this trophy?

    a)   Wigan b) Chelsea c) Barcelona

9. What position were Man Utd in the Premier League when Moyes was sacked?

    a)   4th b) 7th c) 11th

10. Which Spanish team did he manage after leaving Man Utd.

   a)   Valencia   b) Real Sociedad   c) Deportivo La Coruna

QUIZ 6: OLE SOLSKJAER

1.   What year was Solskjaer born?

   a)   1971   b) 1973   c) 1975

2.   What nationality is Solskjaer?

   a)   Swedish   b) Finish   c) Norwegian

3.   How many international games did he play for this country?

   a)   43   b) 67   c) 82

4.   In 1996 Man Utd signed him from Clausenengen. What was the fee?

   a)   £1.5m   b) £7.5m   c) £15m

5.   How many Premier League titles did he win for Man Utd as a player?

   a) 5   b) 6   c) 7

6.   How many goals did he score for Man Utd?

   a)   98   b) 115   c) 127

7.   In 2010 he signed a contract with which club to become their manager?

   a)   Rosenborg BK   b) Malmo   c) Molde

8.   On the 2ⁿᵈ January 2014 he signed to manage which Premier League team?

   a)   Cardiff   b) Swansea   c) Crystal Palace

9. On 19th December 2018 he was appointed caretaker manager of Man Utd. How many games did it take before he was appointed the full-time manager?

    a) 15 b) 17 c) 19

10. How many of these games had Man Utd won?

    a) 8 b) 12 c) 14

QUIZ 7: LOUIS VAN GAAL

1. What year was van Gaal born?

    a) 1949 b) 1951 c) 1953

2. Which team did he start his managerial career with?

    a) Ajax b) Twente   c) PSV Eindhoven

3. In 1995 van Gaal won the Champions League with this team. Who did they beat in the final?

    a) AC Milan   b) Juventus c) Barcelona

4. In 1997 he moved to manage Barcelona. Which British manager did he take over from?

    a) Terry Venables b) Bobby Robson c) Ron Atkinson

5. How many times did he win La Liga with Barcelona?

    a) 1 b) 2 c) 3

6. He was manager of the Netherlands team in the 2014 World Cup. Where did they finish in the competition?

    a) 2nd b) 3rd c) 4th

7. What year did he become Man Utd manager?

    a) 2014 b) 2015 c) 2016

8. Who were his first opponents?

  a) Barnsley b) Barcelona c) LA Galaxy

9. What did van Gaal win two days before he was sacked?

  a) FA Cup b) Manager of the month c) Europa Cup

10. How many games was he in charge of Man Utd?

  a) 99 b) 101 c) 103

QUIZ 8: SIR BOBBY CHARLTON

1. What year was Sir Bobby born?

  a) 1935 b) 1937 c) 1939

2. What was the name of his brother who played for Leeds United and England?

  a) Jim b) Alex c) Jack

3. When did he make his debut for Man Utd?

  a) 1956 b) 1957 c) 1958

4. Who were the opponents when Charlton received his only international booking?

  a) West Germany b) Scotland c) Argentina

5. How many goals did Charlton score in the successful 1966 World Cup Finals?

  a) 1 b) 2 c) 3

6. Who did he play against in his last game for Man Utd?

  a) Southampton b) Chelsea c) Everton

7. How many appearances did he make for Man Utd?

  a) 603 b) 698 c) 758

8. How many goals did he score for Man Utd?
   a) 238 b) 249 c) 261

9. How many First Division league titles did he win with Man Utd?
   a)1 b) 2 c) 3

10. Which team did he play for after he left Man Utd?
    a) Preston NE b) Bury c) Stockport County

QUIZ 9: GEORGE BEST

1. Which country did George Best play for?
   a) England b) Scotland c) Northern Ireland

2. He made his First Division debut aged 17 for Man Utd in which year?
   a) 1962 b) 1963 c)1964

3. How many appearances did he make for Man Utd?
   a) 323 b) 416 c) 470

4. How many goals did he score for them?
   a) 179 b) 201 c) 243

5. Which year was he the First Division's leading scorer?
   a) 1967 -68 b) 1968 -69 c) 1969 – 70

6. In 1976 which American team did he play for?
   a) Philadelphia Atoms b) San Jose Earthquakes c) Los Angeles Aztecs

7. In 1976 -78 he played for which London club?
   a) Fulham b) West Ham c) Tottenham

8. How many times did he win the First Division title with Man Utd?
    a) Once b) Twice c) Three times

9. In 1979 -81 he played for which Scottish club?
    a) Queen of the South b) Aberdeen c) Hibernian

10. In which year did George die?
    a) 2003 b) 2005 c) 2007

Quiz 10: Denis Law

1. Which was Law's first professional club?
    a) Huddersfield b) Aberdeen c) Man City

2. Who did Man Utd sign Denis Law from?
    a) Man City b) Aberdeen c) Torino

3. He was bought for a then British record transfer fee. What was the fee?
    a) £55,000 b) £115,000 c) £145,000

4. How many appearances did he make for Man Utd?
    a) 238 b) 356 c) 404

5. How many goals did he score in those games?
    a) 156 b) 237 c) 294

6. Denis Law holds the record for the most United goals in all competitions in a single season. How many is it?
    a) 46 b) 48 c) 50

7. There is a statue outside Old Trafford honouring the strike force of Denis Law, George Best and Bobby Charlton. What is it titled?

   a) The Three Amigos   b) The United Three   c) The United Trinity

8. Denis Law is the joint record goal scorer for Scotland with 30 goals. Who does he share the record with?

   a) Kenny Dalglish b) Ally McCoist c) Andy Gray

9. Which international footballer's father named his son after his hero Denis Law?

   a) Denis Irwin b) Dennis Bergkamp c) Denis Glushakov

10. What year did Denis Law retire in?

   a) 1972   b) 1973   c) 1974

QUIZ 11: PAUL POGBA

1. What nationality is Pogba?

   a) Belgian b) French c) Italian

2. Growing up which team did he support?

   a) Arsenal   b) Manchester United c) Salford

3. What year did Pogba join Man Utd?

   a) 2009   b) 2014   c) 2016

4. When he left United for Juventus what was the transfer fee?

   a) £0.8m   b) £5m   c) £13m

5. How many Serie A titles did he win with Juventus?

   a) 2 b) 3   c) 4

6. When he re-signed for United how much did they have to pay for him?

    a) £56 m b) £79m c) £89m

7. Who was the manager when Pogba was re-signed?

    a) David Moyes b) Louis van Gaal c) Jose Mourinho

8. Pogba was part of the Man Utd team that won the Europa League in 2016 – 17. Who did they beat in the final?

    a) Lyon b) Ajax c) Celta Vigo

9. He has an agreement with a sportswear company and wears their boots. Which company?

    a) Adidas b) Puma c) Nike

10. Pogba won a world cup medal in 2018. What was the score that they beat Croatia by?

    a) 2 – 1 b) 3 – 2 c) 4 -2

QUIZ 12: BRYAN ROBSON

1. Where was Bryan Robson born?

    a) Chester-Le-Street b) Newcastle c) Hartlepool

2. Which team did Man Utd sign Robson from?

    a) Newcastle b) Sunderland c) West Brom

3. Who was the manager when he was signed?

    a) Dave Sexton b) Ron Atkinson c) Sir Alex Ferguson

4. How many appearances did he make for Man Utd?

    a) 386 b) 432 c) 461

5. How many goals did he score for them?

    a) 90 b) 99 c) 106

6. **How many Premier League titles did he win at Man Utd?**
    a) One b) Two c) Three

7. **Which national team did he manage?**
    a) Thailand b) Vietnam c) Japan

8. **How many times was he captain of England?**
    a) 26 b) 45 c) 63

9. **Which team was he player manager for?**
    a) Middlesbrough b) Bradford City c) Sheffield United

10. **In March 2008 he returned to Man Utd to work in what role?**
    a) Reserve Team Coach b) Ambassador c) Assistant Manager

QUIZ 13: ERIC CANTONA

1. **Where was Cantona born?**
    a) Paris b) Marseille c) Nantes

2. **What was unusual about his family home?**
    *a) It didn't have a bathroom   b) It was a railway carriage
    c) It was a cave*

3. **What was his first professional club?**
    a) Auxerre b) PSG c) Lyon

4. **In 1984 his football career was put on hold. Why?**
    *a) He was in prison b) He trained to become a monk c) He did
    National Service*

5. **In January 1992 he was signed by Leeds United. What was the
transfer fee?**
    a) £1m   b) £12m   c) £22m

6. **What did he win playing for Leeds United?**
    a) FA Cup b) League Cup c) First Division

7. **On 26th November 1992 Cantona signed for Man Utd. Who were his first opponents?**
    a) Arsenal b) Reading c) Benfica

8. **How many league titles did he win with Man Utd?**
    a) 2 b) 3 c) 4

9. **How old was he when he retired?**
    a) 30 b) 31 c) 32

10. **What is his occupation now?**
    a) Psychologist b) Actor c) Wine taster

QUIZ 14: OLD TRAFFORD

1. **When was United's inaugural game at Old Trafford?**
    a) 1898 b) 1906 c) 1910

2. **Who was the game against?**
    a) Liverpool b) Everton c) Celtic

3. **What is the record attendance at Old Trafford?**
    a) 74,287 b) 76,962 c) 78,461

4. **What is the lowest attendance for a competitive game?**
    a) 10,782 b) 11,968 c) 12,341

5. **Which stand has the largest capacity?**
    a) Sir Alex Ferguson Stand b) Stretford End c) Sir Bobby Charlton

6. In October 1993 there was a WBO – WBC Super-Middleweight unification boxing match. Who was the winner?

   a) Joe Calzaghe b) Chris Eubank c) Nigel Benn

7. How big is the field size at Old Trafford?

   a) 102m x 59m b) 103m x 61m c) 105m x 68m

8. From 1941 – 49 Man Utd couldn't play at Old Trafford. Why was this?

   a) Bomb damage b) The ground was requisitioned for military use c) The ground was required for vegetables during the war in the 'Dig for Britain' campaign

9. Where did they play during this period?

   a) Anfield b) Maine Road c) Goodison Park

10. The record Man Utd win at Old Trafford was 9 - 0. Who were the opponents?

    a) Ipswich b) Southampton c) Leicester

QUIZ 15: 1960's TRANSFERS

1. In 1966 Man Utd signed which player from Chelsea for £55,000? He went on to play 433 games for Man Utd, scoring 2 goals.

   a) Harry Greg b) Alex Stepney c) Maurice Setters

2. In July 1961 United signed David Herd from which club for £35,000?

   a) Arsenal b) Chelsea c) Tottenham

3. Which player was sold by United in 1963 to Leeds United for £33,000?

   a) Johnny Giles b) Paul Madeley c) Jack Charlton

4. In 1964 United bought Willie Morgan from which club?

    a) Watford b) Liverpool c) Burnley

5. In January 1960 United signed a player from West Brom for £30,000. Who was it?

    a) Nobby Stiles b) Maurice Setters c) Michael Pinner

6. In November 1960 United signed which Republic of Ireland international from West Ham for £29,500?

    a) Noel Cantwell b) Ian Moir c) Tony Dunne

7. In January 1962 United sold a survivor of the Munich Air Disaster who had scored 179 goals in 293 games. Who was he?

    a) Albert Scanlon b) Ron Cope c) Dennis Violet

8. In April 1964 Man Utd signed a player who had won a league champions medal with Burnley and went on to win another with Man Utd. Who was he?

    a) Graham Moore b) John Connelly c) William Anderson

9. Which centre half was signed by Wilf McGuinness in August 1969 from Arsenal.

    a) Frank McClintock b) Terry Neil c) Ian Ure

10. In 1964 United sold a goalkeeper dubbed 'The Hero of Munich' for pulling teammates from the crashed plane, including Bobby Charlton. Who was this?

    a) Harry Greg b) Jimmy Rimmer c) Pat Dunne

Quiz 16: 1970's Transfers

1. **On the 29th February 1972 Man Utd signed a defender from Aberdeen for £120k who would go on to make 456 appearances for the club. Who was he?**
   a) Bill Foulkes b) Martin Buchan c) Arthur Albiston

2. **In 1971 Man United sold World Cup hero Nobby Stiles for £20,000 to which club?**
   a) Middlesbrough b) Sunderland c) Preston North End

3. **On the 27th September 1972 United signed a prolific goal scorer from Bournemouth. Who was he?**
   a) Ian Storey-Moore b) Ron Davies c) Ted MacDougall

4. **In December 1972 United signed George Graham for £120,000 from which club?**
   a) Arsenal b) Aston Villa c) West Brom

5. **Stuart Pearson was bought by Man Utd in May 1974 for £200,000 and was instrumental in scoring the goals that got the team out of the Second Division. Where was he acquired from?**
   a) Leeds b) Barnsley c) Hull

6. **In 1975 Man Utd signed a player who was studying for an economics degree and went on to play 322 games for the club. Who was he?**
   a) Steve Coppell b) Jimmy Nicholl c) David McCreery

7. **In February 1978 Man Utd paid which club £495,000 for the services of Gordon McQueen?**
   a) Leeds Utd b) St Mirren c) Aberdeen

8. **In 1979 who did Man Utd sign from Chelsea for £833,000?**
   a) Brian Greenhoff b) Kevin Moran C) Ray Wilkins

9. Which forward was signed for £378,0000 in January 1978 from Leeds Utd?

    a) Joe Jordan b) Frank Stapleton c) Remi Moses

10. In January 1976 Man Utd sold a player to Huddersfield who subsequently went on to play cricket for England. Who was he?

    a) Chris Balderstone b) Arnie Sidebottom c) Ian Botham

QUIZ 17: 1980'S TRANSFERS

1. On the 1st October 1981 Man Utd bought Bryan Robson from which club?

    a) Everton   b) Sunderland   c) West Brom

2. Which player did United sign from League of Ireland side St Patrick's Athletic in 1982?

    a) Paul McGrath b) Norman Whiteside c) Anto Whelan

3. Who did United sign from Arsenal in 1981 for £900,000 after previously turning him down as an apprentice?

    a) Remi Moses b) John Gidman c) Frank Stapleton

4. In August 1984 United paid Aberdeen £500,000 for which feisty Scotsman?

    a) Lou Macari b) Gordon Strachan c) Alan Brazil

5. On the 17th December 1987 United bought Steve Bruce from which club?

    a) Norwich   b) Newcastle c) Celtic

6. On the 14th September 1989 Paul Ince was signed from which club for £1m?

    a) West Brom b) Inter Milan c) West Ham

7. In June 1988 United signed which YTS player from Torquay United for £200,000?

   a) Lee Sharpe b) Neil Webb c) Mark Bosnich

8. In 1984 United sold Ray Wilkins to which Italian club for £1.5m?

   a) Juventus b) Lazio c) Inter Milan

9. In July 1987 United signed which forward for £850,000 who would go on to play 355 times for the club scoring 88 goals?

   a) Danny Wallace b) Brian McClair c) Mark Hughes

10. In 1989 Alex Ferguson sold Norman Whiteside to which club?

   a) Everton b) Man City c) West Ham

QUIZ 18: 1990's TRANSFERS

1. In 1990 United signed Dennis Irwin for £625,000 from which club?

   a) Burnley b) Oldham c) Bury

2. Alex Ferguson made a key signing on the 6th August 1991 with the acquisition of Peter Schmeichel from which club?

   a) Brondby b) Hobro c) Horsens

3. On the 7th August 1992 United paid £1m to Cambridge for who?

   a) Mark Robbins b) Les Sealey c) Dion Dublin

4. In 1993 United paid a British transfer record to Notts Forest for Roy Keane. What did they pay?

   a) £3.75m b) 5.75m c) 7.75m

5. On the 10th January 1995 United signed Andy Cole from Newcastle. They paid £6m plus a United player went to Newcastle. Who was the player who departed for Newcastle?

    a) Robbie Savage b) Mike Phelan c) Keith Gillespie

6. On the 29th July 1996 Alex Ferguson signed Ole Solskjaer from which club?

    a) Molde b) Malmo c) Ajax

7. United signed Teddy Sheringham in June 1997 from which club?

    a) Notts Forest b) Spurs c) Millwall

8. In 1998 United bought a player from Eindhoven. He would stay for 3 seasons and won 3 Premier League titles. Who was he?

    a) Jesper Blomquist b) Karl Poborsky c) Jaap Stam

9. On the 20th August 1998 United signed a player from Aston Villa who would win the Premier League, the Champions League and the FA Cup in his first season. Who was it?

    a) Andy Cole b) Dwight Yorke c) Mark Bosnich

10. Who did United sell to Middlesbrough for £2.5m in July 1998?

    a) Gary Pallister b) Ronnie Wallwork c) Jordi Cryuff

Quiz 19: 2000's Transfers

1. Which goalkeeper joined United from Monaco in 2001?
   a) Fabien Barthez b) Andy Goram c) Mark Bosnich

2. In August 2001 Ferguson finally managed to sign long term target Laurent Blanc from Inter. How old was he when he signed for United?
   a) 33   b) 35 c) 37

3. In 2001 United signed a forward who would go on to play 150 games for them scoring a total of 95 goals. Who was he?
   a) Diego Forlan b) Juan Veron c) Ruud van Nistelrooy

4. 2003 saw the arrival of Ronaldo to Old Trafford. From which club was he acquired?
   a) Sporting CP b) Benfica c) Porto

5. Ronaldo inherited the number 7 shirt from David Beckham who left for which club?
   a) Barcelona b) LA Galaxy c) Real Madrid

6. In August 2004 Sir Alex signed Wayne Rooney from Everton. How old was Rooney at the time?
   a) 18 years old b) 19 years old c) 20 years old

7. Edwin van der Sar was signed from Fulham in what year?
   a) 2003 b) 2004 c) 2005

8. On the 31st July 2006 United acquired Michael Carrick from which club?
   a) Spurs b) West Ham c) Everton

9. Dimitar Berbatov was acquired from Spurs for £30m in which year?
   a) 2008 b) 2009 c) 2010

10. In July 2004 United sold Nicky Butt for £2.5m to which club?

   a) Everton   b) Sunderland   c) Newcastle

QUIZ 20: 2010's TRANSFERS

1. On the 27ᵗʰ January 2010 United bought Chris Smalling from which club?

   a) Southampton   b) Fulham   c) Crystal Palace

2. On the 29ᵗʰ June 2011 United bought David de Gea from Atletico Madrid for a record fee for a goalkeeper. How much was the fee?

   a) £18.9m   b) £25.6m   c) £32.3m

3. On the 25ᵗʰ January 2013 United signed Wilfred Zaha from Crystal Palace. How many league games did he play for United before he was sold back to Palace 18 months later?

   a) 0   b) 2   c) 4

4. On the 17ᵗʰ August 2012 United signed Robin van Persie from Arsenal. He played for United 86 times and scored how many goals?

   a) 32   b) 41   c) 48

5. In September 2013 David Moyes signed Marouane Fellaini from his former club Everton. He was sold in January 2019 to which club?

   a) Lyon   b) Borussia Dortmund   c) Shandong Luneng

6. On 26ᵗʰ August 2014 United set a then British record transfer fee of £59.7m for Angel di Maria from Real Madrid. He left about a year later having scored how many league goals for United?

   a) 3   b) 5   c) 7

7. The 1st September 2015 saw Anthony Martial arrive at Old Trafford from which club?

    a) PSG   b) Lyon   c) Monaco

8. On 10th June 2017 United signed Victor Lindelof from Benfica. Which country does he play for?

    a) Sweden   b) Norway   c) Finland

9. On the 10th July 2017 United signed Romelu Lukaku from Everton. Which forward left the club the day before?

    a) Henrikh Mkhitaryan   b) Wayne Rooney   c) Angel di Maria

10. On the 5th June 2018 United signed Fred from Shakhtar Donetsk. Which country is this club in?

    a) Bulgaria   b) Romania   c) Ukraine

Quiz 21: First Division Winners 1956 – 57

1. Man Utd won the First Division title in 1956 -57 season. Who finished second?

    a) Spurs   b) Preston NE   c) Blackpool

2. Who was their leading league goal scorer in the season?

    a) Dennis Violet   b) Bobby Charlton   c) Tommy Taylor

3. Man Utd almost did the double this season but were beaten by which club in the FA Cup final?

    a) Arsenal   b) Aston Villa   c) Bolton

4. United were handicapped during the game by what?

    a) Dennis Violet was sent off   b) Five players were missing due to flu   c) Goalkeeper Ray Wood was injured

5. Who was the United manager during the 56 – 57 season?

    a) Sir Matt Busby b) Jimmy Murphy c) Wilf McGuinness

6. Who made their league debut on the 6th October 1956 against Charlton Athletic?

    a) Tommy Taylor b) Dennis Violet c) Sir Bobby Charlton

7. United also played in the European Cup and lost in the semi-finals to which team?

    a) Barcelona b) Real Madrid c) Juventus

8. In which game during the season did they play in front of the largest number of spectators?

    a) The FA Cup Final b) The European Semi Final c) European Cup Quarter Final against Athletic Bilbao

9. United's first three European home games were played at Maine Road. Why was this?

    a) Old Trafford didn't have floodlights b) A stand had been damaged in high winds c) They had to fulfill a contract with Man City

10. In the preliminary round of the European Cup on the 12th September 1956 they beat a team 10 – 0. Who were the unfortunate victims?

    a) Malmo b) Inter Milan c) Anderlecht

Quiz 22: First Division Winners 1964 – 65

1. United lost at home, their only home defeat of the season, to the eventual second placed team in 1964 -65 season. Which team was this?
   a) Leeds United b) Chelsea c) Everton

2. First and second place were equal on points. How was the title was decided on what?
   a) Goal difference b) Goal Average c) Goal ratio

3. Who scored the most league goals for United during the season?
   a) Bobby Charlton b) George Best c) Denis Law

4. United's biggest win of the season was a home victory over which unfortunate victims?
   a) Aston Villa b) Birmingham c) Wolves

5. United reached the semi-finals of the FA Cup this season. Which team beat them in a semi-final replay?
   a) Leeds b) Everton c) Liverpool

6. They also reached the semi-finals of the Inter-Cities Fairs Cup but were beaten by which team?
   a) Real Madrid b) Borussia Dortmund c) Ferencvaros

7. What was one of the qualifying conditions to enter the Inter-City Fairs Cup?
   a) The team had to finish in the top half of the Fair Play League. b) The city had to host a trade fair c) They had to finish third in their domestic league

8. Who was Chairman of the club during the 64 – 65 season?
   a) Harold Hardman b) James W Gibson c) Louis Edwards

9. Who was the defender who played every game in the season and a total of 688 games for United?

   a) Pat Crerand   b) Bill Foulkes   c) Nobby Stiles

10. Which United player won the European Footballer of the Year (Ballon d'Or) in 1964?

    a) Bobby Charlton   b) George Best   c) Denis Law

Quiz 23: European Champions 1967 - 68

1. Who were the defending champions in the European competition of 1967 – 68?

   a) Real Madrid   b) Bayern Munich   c) Celtic

2. Who was the leading goal scorer in the competition?

   a) Eusebio   b) Denis Law   c) Bobby Charlton

3. Who did Man Utd play in the final?

   a) Juventus   b) Benfica   c) Real Madrid

4. The final was won 4 – 1 by United. Charlton got two goals, George Best one and who scored the other?

   a) David Sadler   b) John Aston   c) Brian Kidd

5. In the first round United played Hibernians. Which country are they based in?

   a) Ireland   b) Scotland   c) Malta

6. Which ground was the final played at?

   a) Camp Nou   b) Wembley   c) Ibrox

7. Who was the United goalkeeper in the final?

   a) Alex Stepney   b) Jimmy Rimmer   c) Harry Gregg

8. Who was the only Scotsman in the United team?

   a) Tony Dunne b) Denis Law c) Pat Crerand

9. In defending their cup in the 1968 – 69 competition they were beaten by whom?

   a) Anderlecht b) Barcelona c) AC Milan

10. How many United players who played in the winning 1968 final were also survivors of the terrible Munich air crash in 1958?

    a) 1 b) 2 c) 3

QUIZ 24: FA CUP WINNERS 1977

1. Who did Man Utd play in the 1977 FA Cup final?

   a) Everton b) Man City c) Liverpool

2. What was the score?

   a) 1 – 0 b) 2 – 1 c) 3 – 2

3. Who was United's leading goal scorer in the FA Cup run of 1976 -77?

   a) Jimmy Greenhoff b) Stuart Pearson c) Gordon Hill

4. Who did United beat in the semi-final?

   a) Liverpool b) Everton c) Leeds United

5. How many substitutes were allowed in the final?

   a) 0 b) 1 c) 3

6. Who was United's captain in the final?

   a) Martin Buchan b) Brian Greenhoff c) Jimmy Nicholl

7. Who was the United Manager during the cup run?

   a) Frank O'Farrell b) Tommy Docherty c) Dave Sexton

8. Lou Macari scored the winner which was a deflected shot which looped over Ray Clemence in the Liverpool goal. Who did Macari's shot deflect off?

    a) Jimmy Greenhoff b) Brian Greenhoff c) Stuart Pearson

9. Man Utd's victory in the Cup Final prevented Liverpool doing the treble of FA Cup, First Division and European Cup. How many years later did Man Utd achieve this treble for themselves?

    a) 17 seasons   b) 19 seasons   c) 22 seasons

10. Who was the substitute that United used in the final?

    a) David McCreery b) Gordon Hill c) Arthur Albiston

QUIZ 25: FA CUP WINNERS 1985

1. Who did Man Utd beat to win the 1985 cup final?

    a)   Spurs   b) Everton   c) Watford

2. United won 1 – 0 (AET). Who scored the goal?

    a)   Norman Whiteside b) Bryan Robson c) Mark Hughes

3. This FA Cup final saw the first sending off in an FA Cup Final. Who was the offender?

    a)   Mark Hughes b) Kevin Moran c) John Gidman

4. Who was the United manager at the final?

    a)   Ron Atkinson b) Dave Sexton c) Alex Ferguson

5. Who was the only United player to have played in the winning United team in the 1977 FA Cup final?

    a)   Gary Bailey   b) Bryan Robson c) Arthur Albiston

6. **Jesper Olsen played in the final for United. What nationality is he?**
    a) Swedish   b) Norwegian   c) Danish

7. **Which team did they beat in a semi-final replay to reach the FA Cup final?**
    a) Everton   b) Liverpool   c) West Ham

8. **United won the game 2 – 1. The opposition goal was an own goal scored by who?**
    a) Norman Whiteside b) Paul McGrath c) Kevin Moran

9. **Who was the leading goal scorer for United in their 1984 - 85 FA Cup run?**
    a) Gordon Strachan b) Norman Whiteside c) Bryan Robson

10. **Who was the United captain for the final?**
    a) Bryan Robson b) Paul McGrath c) Mark Hughes

QUIZ 26: PREMIER LEAGUE WINNERS 1992 -93

1. **The 1992 – 93 season was the inaugural year of the Premier League. How many teams were in the League?**
    a) 18   b) 20   c) 22

2. **Which club finished second?**
    a) Aston Villa   b) Liverpool   c) Arsenal

3. **Who were United's first opponents in the newly formed Premier League?**
    a) Norwich b) Ipswich c) Sheff Utd

4. **Who was United's top league goal scorer?**
    a) Brian McClair   b) Eric Cantona   c) Mark Hughes

5. Who were United's kit manufacturer for the 1992 – 93 season?

    a) Umbro   b) Admiral   c) Adidas

6. The broadcasting rights for the new league were bought by Sky and the BBC. How much did they have to pay?

    a) £305m   b) £824m   c) £1.2bn

7. Which United player was voted the PFA Young Player of the Year?

    a) David Beckham   b) Ryan Giggs   c) Nicky Butt

8. Which United player scored the first ever Premier League hat trick?

    a) Eric Cantona   b) Mark Hughes   c) Brian McClair

9. On the 7th August 1992 United paid £1m for Dion Dublin from which club?

    a) Norwich   b) Cambridge   c) Coventry

10. Two players started every league game for United. One was Steve Bruce, who was the other?

    a) Gary Pallister   b) Ryan Giggs   c) Denis Irwin

QUIZ 27: THE TREBLE 1998 – 99

1. Who finished second in the Premier League to Man Utd?

    a) Leeds Utd   b) Arsenal   c) Chelsea

2. Which team did United beat 8 -1 away from home in a league game?

    a) Notts Forest   b) Derby   c) Middlesbrough

3. Who was United's shirt sponsor in this season?

    a) *Carlsberg* b) *Cellnet* c) *Sharp*

4. Who did United beat in the final of the FA Cup in 1999?

    a) *Newcastle* b) *Liverpool* c) *Fulham*

5. They were denied the quadruple because they were beaten in the League Cup by which team?

    a) *Notts Forest* b) *Arsenal* c) *Spurs*

6. Where was the European Cup final played?

    a) *Barcelona* b) *Milan* c) *Paris*

7. Who did United beat in the semi-finals of the European Cup?

    a) *Juventus* b) *Inter Milan* c) *Real Madrid*

8. Who was the leading overall goal scorer for Man Utd in the Treble season?

    a) *Andy Cole* b) *Dwight Yorke* c) *Ole Solskjaer*

9. Who was the United captain for the season?

    a) *Denis Irwin* b) *Jaap Stam* c) *Roy Keane*

10. How many trophies and titles did Man Utd win the previous season?

    a) *0* b) *1* c) *2*

Quiz 28: Premier League Champions 2002 -03

1. Who finished as runners up to Man Utd?

    a) Arsenal b) Liverpool c) Newcastle

2. Who was the leading League goal scorer?

    a) Scholes b) van Nistelrooy c) Solksjaer

3. On the 22nd July 2002 United broke the English transfer record to sign who?

    a) Roy Keane b) Rio Ferdinand c) Juan Veron

4. Who was United's first choice goalkeeper for the season?

    a) Raymond van der Gouw b) Tim Howard c) Fabien Barthez

5. Who was their shirt sponsor for the season?

    a) Vodaphone b) Betfair c) Carlsberg

6. What nationality was the Man Utd captain for the season?

    a) English b) Irish c) Welsh

7. United played their last game at which ground this season?

    a) Maine Road b) Highbury c) Ayresome Park

8. Which United player made the most appearances as a substitute in the league in 2002 - 03?

    a) Ole Solskjaer b) Diego Forlan c) Wes Brown

9. Which player played their last game for United this season?

    a) Wes Brown b) Ruud van Nistelrooy c) David Beckham

10. United's biggest win of the season was a 6 – 2 away win against which club?

    a) Newcastle b) Sunderland c) Birmingham

QUIZ 29: EUROPEAN CHAMPIONS LEAGUE 2007 - 08

1. **Who did United play in the final?**
    a) *AC Milan* b) *Bayern Munich* c) *Chelsea*

2. **Who were the defending champions?**
    a) *AC Milan* b) *Bayern Munich* c) *Chelsea*

3. **Where was the final played?**
    a) *Rome* b) *Paris* c) *Moscow*

4. **Which future Man City player scored against Man Utd in the final?**
    a) *Frank Lampard* b) *Sergio Aguero* c) *Yaya Touré*

5. **Who missed their penalty for Man Utd in the penalty shoot out?**
    a) *Wayne Rooney* b) *Carlos Tevez* c) *Cristiano Ronaldo*

6. **The score in normal time was 1 – 1. Who got United's goal?**
    a) *Wayne Rooney* b) *Carlos Tevez* c) *Cristiano Ronaldo*

7. **Who did United beat in the semi – finals?**
    a) *Barcelona* b) *Real Madrid* c) *AC Milan*

8. **Who was the leading scorer in the 2007 – 08 European Champions League?**
    a) *Ronaldo* b) *Messi* c) *Drogba*

9. **Who was Man Utd's goalkeeper in the final?**
    a) *Tim Howard* b) *Edwin van der Sar* c) *David de Gea*

10. **How many teams competed in the 2007 – 08 Champions League from the Qualifying rounds to the knock-out phase?**
    a) *52* b) *64* c) *76*

QUIZ 30: PREMIER LEAGUE CHAMPIONS 2012 – 13

1. **Who were the Premier League sponsors?**
    a)   Barclays   b) Barclaycard   c) Carling

2. **Who were second to Man Utd in the Premier League of 2012 – 13?**
    a)   Chelsea   b) Arsenal   c) Man City

3. **Who were the defending league champions in this season?**
    a)   Chelsea   b) Man City   c) Arsenal

4. **Including the 2012 – 13 season how many First Division and Premier League titles have Man Utd won?**
    a)   16   b) 18   c) 20

5. **Who was the leading Man Utd league goal scorer in 2012 – 13?**
    a)   Robin van Persie   b) Paul Scholes   c) Ruud van Nistelrooy

6. **Alex Ferguson retired at the end of the season and was the oldest manager in the football league. How old was he when he retired?**
    a)   69   b) 71   c) 73

7. **Ferguson's last game ended in a remarkable 5 – 5 draw. Who was it against?**
    a)   Swansea   b) Aston Villa   c) West Brom

8. **There were four Man Utd players in the PFA player of the year team. Which of the following wasn't in the team?**
    a)   Michael Carrick   b) Ryan Giggs   c) David de Gea

9. **Which team beat them in both the League Cup and FA Cup in the 2012 – 13 season?**
    a)   Chelsea   b) Arsenal   c) Liverpool

10. Who was the only United player to play in all their League games in the 2012 – 13 season?

    a) David de Gea   b) Michael Carrick   c) Robin van Persie

QUIZ 31: FA CUP WINNERS 2015 – 16

1. Who did Man Utd beat in the 2016 FA Cup final?

    a) Fulham   b) Crystal Palace   c) West Ham

2. This was a repeat of which year's final?

    a) 1977   b) 1990   c) 2004

3. What was the score, after extra time, of the 2016 final?

    a) 2 – 1   b) 3 – 1   c) 3 – 2

4. Who scored United's winning goal?

    a) Rooney   b) Rashford   c) Lingard

5. A United player became the fourth player to be sent off in an FA Cup final when he got a second yellow card. Who was this?

    a) Smalling   b) Fellaini   c) Carrick

6. Who did Man Utd beat in the semi-final to reach the final?

    a) West Ham   b) Liverpool   c) Everton

7. In the semi final David de Gea saved a penalty taken by whom?

    a) Lukaku   b) Barkley   c) Deulofeu

8. Who was the Man Utd manager?

    a) David Moyes   b) Louis van Gaal   c) Jose Mourinho

9. This win equalled Arsenal's record number of FA Cup Trophy wins. How many is that?

    a) 10   b) 12   c) 14

10. Who was the Ecuadorian who played for Man Utd in the final?

    a) *Antonio Valencia*   *b) Marcos Rojo*   *c) Matteo Darmian*

QUIZ 32: CLUB CAPTAINS

1. Who was the Man Utd captain in 1982?

    a) *Martin Buchan*   *b) Ray Wilkins*   *c)* *Gordon McQueen*

2. Who was the Man Utd captain from1983 to 1994?

    a) *Bryan Robson*   *b) Gordon Strachan*   *c) Paul McGrath*

3. Who was the Man Utd captain from 1994 to 1996?

    a) *Steve Bruce*   *b) Paul Ince*   *c) Gary Pallister*

4. Who was Man Utd captain from 1996 to 1997?

    a) *Denis Irwin*   *b) David May*   *c) Eric Cantona*

5. Who was Man Utd captain from 1997 to 2005?

    a) *Roy Keane*   *b) Rio Ferdinand*   *c) Ryan Giggs*

6. Who was Man Utd captain from 2005 to 2011?

    a) *Michael Carrick*   *b) Paul Scholes*   *c) Gary Neville*

7. Who was Man Utd captain from 2011 to 2014?

    a) *Robin van Persie*   *b) Nemanja Vidic*   *c) Patrice Evra*

8. Who was Man Utd captain from 2014 to 2017?

    a) *Juan Mata*   *b) Morgan Schneiderlin*   *c) Wayne Rooney*

9. Who was Man Utd captain from 2017 to 2018?

    a) *Michael Carrick*   *b) Paul Pogba*   *c) David de Gea*

10. Who was Man Utd captain from 2018?

    a) *Ashley Young*   *b) Antonio Valencia*   *c) Victor Lindelof*

QUIZ 33: SIR MATT BUSBY PLAYER OF THE YEAR

1. **Who was player of the season in 1988 – 89?**
   a) *Paul McGrath* b) *Mark Hughes* c) *Bryan Robson*

2. **Who was player of the season in 1993 – 94?**
   a) *Eric Cantona* b) *Paul Ince* c) *Roy Keane*

3. **Who was player of the season in 1996 – 97?**
   a) *Peter Schmeichel* b) *David Beckham* c) *Paul Scholes*

4. **Who was player of the season in 1997 – 98?**
   a) *Ryan Giggs* b) *Teddy Sheringham* c) *Henning Berg*

5. **Who was player of the season in 2001 – 02?**
   a) *Gary Neville* b) *Juan Veron* c) *Teddy Sheringham*

6. **Who was player of the season in 2002 – 03?**
   a) *Fabian Barthez* b) *Ruud van Nistelrooy* c) *Laurent Blanc*

7. **Who was player of the season in 2007 – 08?**
   a) *Cristiano Ronaldo* b) *Carlos Tevez* c) *Wes Brown*

8. **Who was player of the season in 2009 – 10?**
   a) *Dimitar Berbatov* b) *Edwin van der Sar* c) *Wayne Rooney*

9. **Who was player of the season in 2015 – 16?**
   a) *David de Gea* b) *Anthony Martial* c) *Ander Herrera*

10. **Who was player of the season in 2018 – 19?**
    a) *Romelu Lukaku* b) *Ashley Young* c) *Luke Shaw*

QUIZ 34: RUUD VAN NISTELROOY

1. **Who did Man Utd buy Nistelrooy from?**
    a) PSV Eindhoven   b) Ajax   c) Heerenveen

2. **His transfer was due in the summer of 2000 but was delayed for a year for what reason?**
    a) Contractual issue with the player   b) Man Utd had signed someone else   c) Fitness concerns

3. **In 2002 – 03 he was the Premier League's leading goal scorer with how many goals?**
    a) 22   b) 25   c) 28

4. **In 2003 – 04 he set a then Premier League record by scoring in how many league games consecutively?**
    a) 9   b) 10   c) 11

5. **How many Premier League games did he play for United?**
    a) 120   b) 140   c) 150

6. **How many Premier League goals did he score in these games.**
    a) 95   b) 103   c) 108

7. **In July 2006 Nistelrooy left United for which club?**
    a) Real Madrid   b) Malaga   c) Hamburg

8. **How many times did he win the Premier League with United?**
    a) 1   b) 2   c) 3

9. **How many times was he the Champions League leading goal scorer?**
    a) 1   b) 2   c) 3

10. What was the total number of goals in all competitions Nistelrooy got in his five seasons with United?

    a)   145   b) 150   c) 155

Quiz 35: Ryan Giggs

1. **Ryan wasn't born with the surname Giggs. What was his birth name?**

    a)   Jones   b) Davies   c) Wilson

2. **Where was Giggs born?**

    a)   Cardiff   b) Swansea   c) Wrexham

3. **Giggs' father was a professional at what sport?**

    a)   Rugby   b) Golf   c) football

4. **In what year did he make his debut for Man Utd?**

    a)   1990   b) 1991   c) 1992

5. **Giggs scored the last ever goal in an FA Cup semi-final replay in 1999 as the rules were changed the following season. It was one of his most famous dribbling goals from his own half. Who were the opposition?**

    a)   Leeds   b) Everton   c) Arsenal

6. **How many times did Giggs play for Wales?**

    a)   64   b) 72   c) 76

7. **How many times has Giggs won the Premiership with Man Utd?**

    a)   9   b) 11   c) 13

8. In what year did he win the BBC Sports Personality of the Year?

  a) 2001 b) 2007 c) 2009

9. Giggs holds the record for the number of appearances for Man Utd. How many?

  a) 872 b) 963 c) 984

10. How many goals did he score in those games?

  a) 168 b) 178 c) 188

QUIZ 36: WAYNE ROONEY

1. What is Wayne Rooney's middle name?

  a) Mark b) Walter c) Alex

2. What year did he make his debut for Everton?

  a) 2000 b) 2001 c) 2002

3. Rooney became the leading goal scorer for Man Utd from Sir Bobby Charlton. How many more has he scored than Charlton?

  a) 4 b) 14 c) 24

4. Rooney scored his first international goal in the Euro 2004 qualifiers against which team?

  a) Croatia b) Slovenia c) Macedonia

5. He made his debut for United in the Champions League and scored a hat trick against which team?

  a) Anderlecht b) Fenerbahçe c) Galatasaray

6. Rooney is one of two English players to have won the Champions League, the FA Cup, the Premier League, the League cup, Europa League and FIFA Club World Cup. Who is the other?

    a) David Beckham   b) Paul Scholes   c) Michael Carrick

7. In 2017 Rooney left United and returned to Everton. How many goals did he score for Everton in this second spell?

    a) 8   b) 11   c) 16

8. On the 28th June 2018 Rooney signed for which American team?

    a) DC United   b) LA Galaxy   c) Vancouver Whitecaps

9. How many goals did he score for this team?

    a) 25   b) 27   c) 31

10. In August 2018 which club announced Rooney would be joining them as a player/coach?

    a) Leeds United   b) Aston Villa   c) Derby

QUIZ 37: BILL FOULKES

1. In what year did Foulkes join Man Utd?

    a) 1950   b) 1951   c) 1952

2. In 1954 he was called up to play for England and only after that did he give up his job prior to joining Man Utd. What was his job?

    a) Grocer   b) Butcher   c) Miner

3. How many League Championships did he win with Man Utd?

    a) 3   b) 4   c) 5

4. How many appearances did he make for Man Utd?
    a) 588   b) 688   c) 788

5. How many appearances did he make for England?
    a) 1   b) 21   c) 41

6. What age was he when he retired?
    a) 36   b) 38   c) 40

7. Who was the manager when he retired?
    a) Wilf McGuinness   b) Dave Sexton   c) Frank O'Farrell

8. How many goals did he score for United?
    a) 9   b) 19   c) 29

9. How many FA Cups did he win with United?
    a) 1   b) 2   c) 3

10. In October 1992 he had to sell mementoes and all his medals to raise money. How much did his European Cup medal sell for?
    a) £2,000   b) £11,000   c) £25,000

QUIZ 38: PAUL SCHOLES

1. Scholes is co-owner of Salford FC. What is their nickname?
    a) The Reds   b) The Lowries   c) The Ammies

2. Which team did Scholes support as a youngster?
    a) Oldham   b) Man City   c) Bury

3. What year did he make his debut for the Man Utd 1st XI?
    a) 1993   b) 1994   c) 1995

4. Who did Scholes make his league debut against?

   a) Blackburn   b) Everton   c) Ipswich

5. Scholes is second in the list of those who have received most yellow cards in the Champions League behind Sergio Ramos. How many did he receive?

   a) 20   b) 25   c) 32

6. Scholes missed the 1998 – 99 European Final because he was suspended for a foul on who?

   a) Zidane   b) Deschamps   c) Inzaghi

7. Who did Scholes make his international debut against?

   a) South Africa   b) Slovenia   c) Spain

8. On the 8th January 2012 Scholes reversed a previous decision to retire from football. How long did his first 'retirement' last?

   a) 186 days   b) 222 days   c) 308 days

9. How many league titles did he win with Man Utd?

   a) 10   b) 11   c) 12

10. How may goals did he score for Man Utd?

   a) 143   b) 151   c) 155

QUIZ 39: ROY KEANE

1. **What is Roy Keane's middle name?**
   a) Carroll   b) George   c) Maurice

2. **Which town was he born in?**
   a) Cork   b) Dublin   c) Limerick

3. **What was his first English league club?**
   a) Bury   b) Sheff Utd   c) Notts Forest

4. **What year did Keane join Man Utd?**
   a) 1993   b) 1994   c) 1995

5. **How many red cards did Keane receive while with Man Utd?**
   a) 7   b) 9   c) 11

6. **In 1997 Keane became club captain. Who did he take over from?**
   a) Eric Cantona   b) Bryan Robson   c) Ray Wilkins

7. **On the 15th December 2005 Keane joined which club?**
   a) Celtic   b) Rangers   c) Aberdeen

8. **How many games did he play for the Republic of Ireland?**
   a) 67   b) 74   c) 79

9. **Which club did he start his managerial career at?**
   a) Ipswich   b) Norwich   c) Sunderland

10. **On the 5th November Keane was appointed assistant manager for the Republic of Ireland. Who was the manager?**
    a) Martin O'Neil   b) Steve Staunton   c) Giovanni Trapattoni

QUIZ 40: GARY NEVILLE

1. What was the first name of Gary Neville's father?
   a) Gary   b) Phillip   c) Neville

2. Gary Neville was a good youth cricketer. In a game for his club he scored a century and shared a 200 opening partnership with which Australian cricketer?
   a) Matt Hayden   b) Ricky Ponting   c) Justin Langer

3. What year did Gary Neville make his senior debut for Man Utd?
   a) 1992   b) 1993   c) 1994

4. How many league goals did Neville score for United?
   a) 5   b) 10   c) 15

5. What year was he appointed captain?
   a) 2003   b) 2004   c) 2005

6. Neville's first appearance for England was in 1995. Who was England's manager?
   a) Graham Taylor   b) Terry Venables   c) Glenn Hoddle

7. How many goals did Neville score for England?
   a) 0   b) 1   c) 2

8. On the 2nd December 2015 Neville was appointed manager of which Spanish club?
   a) Valencia   b) Villareal   c) Real Betis

9. How many league titles did he win with Man Utd?
   a) 6   b) 7   c) 8

10. How many appearances did he make for Man Utd?
    a) 592   b) 602   c) 611

QUIZ 41: MARK HUGHES

1. Where was Mark Hughes born?
   a) *Cardiff*   b) *Swansea*   c) *Wrexham*

2. Who was the Man Utd manager when Hughes made his debut?
   a) *Dave Sexton*   b) *Ron Atkinson*   c) *Alex Ferguson*

3. In the summer of 1986 Man Utd sold Hughes to which Spanish club?
   a) *Barcelona*   b) *Real Madrid*   c) *Valencia*

4. This move wasn't a great success and he was loaned out to which German team?
   a) *Eintracht Frankfurt*   b) *Bayern Munich*   c) *Leipzig*

5. In May 1988 he returned to Man Utd for another 7 seasons. How many goals did he score for Man Utd in both spells at the club?
   a) *147*   b) *163*   c) *182*

6. In June 1985 Hughes left United for the final time and was sold to which club?
   a) *Blackburn*   b) *Southampton*   c) *Chelsea*

7. In the 1998 – 99 season Hughes gained the unwanted record of the most yellow cards in a Premier League season by any player. How many did he get?
   a) *10*   b) *12*   c) *14*

8. Which club did he score his last Premier League goal for?
   a) *Blackburn*   b) *Everton*   c) *Southampton*

9. Where was his first managerial appointment?
   a) *Man City*   b) *Blackburn*   c) *Wales*

10. How many Premier League titles did Hughes win?

    a) 1   b) 2   c) 3

QUIZ 42: ALEX STEPNEY

1. Where did Stepney begin his football career as a trainee?

    a) Millwall   b) Watford   c) Arsenal

2. Which club did United buy Stepney from?

    a) Tottenham   b) Chelsea   c) Brentford

3. Sir Matt Busby paid a then world record fee for a goalkeeper. How much was this?

    a) £45,000   b) £55,000   c) £65,000

4. What year was Stepney born?

    a) 1938   b) 1940   c) 1942

5. How many goals has Stepney scored for United?

    a) 0   b) 1   c) 2

6. How many first Division titles did he win with United?

    a) 0   b) 1   c) 2

7. What was the total number of games he played for United?

    a) 431   b) 546   c) 636

8. In 1978 Stepney left United for which club?

    a) Dallas Tornado   b) Tampa Bay Rowdies   c) Tulsa Roughnecks

9. He won an FA Cup medal in 1977 when they beat Liverpool 2 – 1 in the final. Who scored against Stepney?

    a) Kevin Keegan   b) Jimmy Case   c) Steve Heighway

10. Which non-league team did he play for to win the Alliance
    Premier League in 1980 – 81?
    a) Altrincham   b) Salford   c) Barrow

QUIZ 43: DUNCAN EDWARDS

1. Where was Duncan Edwards born?
    a) Salford   b) Bury   c) Dudley

2. Apart from football what else did he represent his school at?
    a) Javelin Throwing   b) Chess   c) Morris Dancing

3. As a back up to his football career Edwards also began an
    apprenticeship as what?
    a) Carpenter   b) Electrician   c) Plumber

4. On the 4th April 1953 he made his debut for United. What was
    his age?
    a) 16 years 185 days   b) 16 years 320 days   c) 17 years 26
    days

5. How many League games did he play for Man Utd?
    a) 151   b) 161   c) 171

6. How much was he paid per week by United?
    a) £15   b) £30   c) £70

7. How many times did he win the League with United?
    a) 0   b) 1   c) 2

8. How many times did he play for England?
    a) 13   b) 18   c) 24

9. Who were the opponents in his last League game?
    a) Arsenal   b) Tottenham   c) Everton

10. Edwards was stopped by police for riding his bike without lights. What action did United take?

    a) Sir Matt Busby gave him a warning b) He had to do an extra training session c) He was fined two weeks wages

QUIZ 44: PREMIER LEAGUE WINNERS 1995 – 96

1. Who finished second to Man Utd in the 1995 – 96 Premier League?

    a) Liverpool   b) Aston Villa   c) Newcastle

2. Man Utd also did the double by winning the FA Cup. Who did they beat in the final?

    a) Everton   b) Newcastle   c) Liverpool

3. They lost their first game in the League Cup this season. Which club beat them?

    a) York   b) Grimsby   c) Sheffield United

4. Who scored the most league goals in the 1995 – 96 season for Man Utd?

    a) Ryan Giggs   b) Eric Cantona   c) Andy Cole

5. Queens Park Rangers and Bolton were two of the teams relegated this season. Who was the other?

    a) Man City   b) West Ham   c) Notts Forest

6. Only one Man Utd player was in the PFA team of the year for the 1995 – 96 season. Who was this?

    a) Peter Schmeichel   b) Eric Cantona   c) Gary Neville

7. Man Utd had the biggest away win of the season when they beat who 6 – 0?

    a) Bolton   b) Queens Park Rangers   c) Wimbledon

8. Who were the Utd shirt sponsors for the season?

   a) AIG   b) Vodafone   c) Sharp

9. United suffered a first round exit in the UEFA Cup to Rotor Volgograd. They did preserve their 39 year unbeaten record in home European ties thanks to a late equalizer by who?

   a) Eric Cantona   b) Andy Cole   c) Peter Schmeichel

10. Who did Man Utd beat 3 – 0 in the last game to clinch the title?

   a) Middlesbrough   b) Blackburn   c) Everton

QUIZ 45: FIRST DIVISION WINNERS 1951 – 52

1. How many years was it since they had won the First Division prior to the 1951 – 52 season?

   a) 32 years   b) 41 years   c) 48 years

2. Who finished second in the League to United?

   a) Portsmouth   b) Arsenal   c) Tottenham

3. Who played for Man Utd this season and their son played for United 13 years later?

   a) John Aston   b) Jack Rowley   c) Jackie Blanchflower

4. Who was the United captain during this season?

   a) Allenby Chilton   b) Johnny Berry   c) Johnny Carey

5. Who was the Man Utd manager in 1951 – 52?

   a) Walter Crickmer   b) Sir Matt Busby   c) Jimmy Murphy

6. Who was signed at the beginning of the season from Birmingham for £25,000?

   a) Johnny Berry   b) Allenby Chilton   c) Stan Pearson

7. Who was the leading League goal scorer for United this season?

   a) Jack Rowley   b) Stan Pearson   c) John Downie

8. United finished the season off with a 6 – 1 thrashing of which team?

   a) Liverpool   b) Chelsea   c) Arsenal

9. Who was the only Irishman in the United team this season?

   a) Johnny Carey   b) Henry Cockburn   c) John Downie

10. Who was the only player to play in every league game for United in 1951 – 52?

    a) Jack Rowley   b) Henry Cockburn   c) Allenby Chilton

QUIZ 46: EUROPA LEAGUE WINNERS 2016 – 17

1. Where was the Europa League Final held?

   a) Stockholm   b) Helsinki   c) Copenhagen

2. Who were United's opponents?

   a) Feyenoord   b) Ajax   c) Anderlecht

3. What was the score by which United won?

   a) 1 – 0   b) 2 – 0   c) 2 – 1

4. Who was the United manager?

   a) Mourinho   b) Moyes   c) Van Gaal

5. Who was the Man of the Match?

   a) Pogba   b) Rashford   c) Herrera

6. Who did United beat in the semi-final?

   a) Celta Vigo   b) Legia Warsaw   c) Lyon

7. Who was the leading goal scorer for United in the Europa Cup in 2016 – 17?

    a) Rooney   b) Ibrahimović   c) Mkhitaryan

8. Which competition didn't they win this season?

    a) FA Cup   b) Community Shield c) EFL Cup

9. Who was Man Utd's captain in the final?

    a) Pogba b) Smalling   c) Valencia

10. Man Utd didn't finish top in their group stage. Which club was top?

    a) Fenerbahçe b) Feyenoord c) Standard Liege

QUIZ 47: 2ND DIVISION CHAMPIONS 1974 – 75

1. How many times had Man Utd been the Second Division Champions before the 1974 – 75 season?

    a) 0 b) 1 c) 2

2. United kept faith with the manager from the previous season. Who was he?

    a) Tommy Docherty   b) Frank O'Farrell   c) Dave Sexton

3. Which club were second to United in the league in 1974 – 75?

    a) Norwich   b) Aston Villa   c) Notts Forest

4. Who was the leading scorer for United?

    a) McIlroy b) Daly   c) Pearson

5. Where had this player been acquired from?

    a) Hull   b) Leeds   c) Aston Villa

6. Who were the First Division champions in this season?

    a) Derby   b) Liverpool   c) Everton

7. Who was the reserve keeper to Alex Stepney in this season?

    a) Gary Bailey   b) Jimmy Rimmer   c) Paddy Roche

8. Who was captain of United this season?

    a) Martin Buchan   b) Willie Morgan   c) George Graham

9. United were knocked out of the League Cup at the semi-final stage by which fellow Second Division team?

    a) Norwich   b) Aston Villa   c) Notts County

10. Despite being in the Second Division United still had the highest average home gates in the country. To the nearest thousand what was their average gate?

    a) 42,000   b) 48,000   c) 55,000

QUIZ 48: FA CUP 1990 WINNERS

1. Who did United beat in the 1990 FA Cup final?

    a) Liverpool   b) Everton   c) Crystal Palace

2. Who scored the winning goal for United in the replay?

    a) Mark Hughes   b) Lee Martin   c) Danny Wallace

3. Who did United beat in the semi-final stage?

    a) Oldham   b) Sheff United   c) Newcastle

4. In the replay Sir Alex picked the same team apart from one player. What position did this player occupy?

    a) Goalkeeper   b) Centre half   c) Centre forward

5. United produced a song to mark their appearance. What was it called?

    a) We will stand together   b) United we love you   c) We all follow Man Utd

6. Which football pundit scored against United in the final?
    a) Mark Bright   b) Ian Wright   c) Alan Pardew

7. How many trophies had Sir Alex Ferguson won for Man Utd before this Fa Cup win?
    a) 0   b) 1   c) 2

8. Where did United finish in the League this season?
    a) 2nd   b) 5th   c) 13th

9. Who was the leading goal scorer for United in the 1989 – 90 season?
    a) Brian McClair   b) Mark Hughes   c) Mark Robbins

10. How many home games did United have in the 1989 – 90 FA Cup campaign?
    a) 0   b) 1   c) 2

QUIZ 49: CHARITY/COMMUNITY SHIELD

1. Who did United beat in the 2016 FA Community Shield?
    a) Leicester   b) Everton   c) Man City

2. Who did United beat in the 2013 FA Community Shield?
    a) Man City   b) Arsenal   c) Wigan

3. Who did United beat in the 2011 FA Community Shield?
    a) Chelsea   b) Liverpool   c) Man City

4. Who did United beat in the 2010 FA Community Shield?
    a) Everton   b) Portsmouth   c) Chelsea

5. Who did United beat in the 2008 FA Community Shield?
    a) Portsmouth   b) Cardiff   c) West Ham

6. Who did United beat in the 2007 FA Community Shield?
   a) Chelsea   b) Arsenal   c) Blackburn

7. Who did United beat in the 2003 FA Community Shield?
   a) Chelsea   b) Southampton   c) Arsenal

8. Who did United beat in the 1997 FA Charity Shield?
   a) Middlesbrough   b) Newcastle   c) Chelsea

9. Who did United beat in the 1996 FA Charity Shield?
   a) Newcastle   b) Liverpool   c) Everton

10. Who did United beat in the 1994 FA Charity Shield?
    a) Everton   b) Blackburn   c) Chelsea

QUIZ 50: MISCELLANEOUS

1. Sir Alex Ferguson has played once for Man Utd against which team?
   a) Bermuda   b) Somerset Cricket Club   c) Antigua

2. Which Man Utd player is the only Scotsman to win the Ballon d'Or?
   a) Pat Crerand   b) Denis Law   c) Martin Buchan

3. What year was Songs of Praise recorded at Old Trafford?
   a) 1992   b) 1993   c) 1994

4. Who was Sir Alex's first signing at Old Trafford?
   a) Jim Leighton   b) Steve Bruce   c) Viv Anderson

5. In the 1973 - 74 season Man Utd were relegated to the 2nd Division. Who scored the winning goal against them in the last game to ensure that they couldn't survive?
   a) Denis Law   b) Brian Kidd   c) Jack Charlton

6. Goalkeeper Nick Culkin made one Premier League appearance for United on 22nd August 1999 against Arsenal. What was unusual about this appearance?

   a) He scored a goal   b) He saved three penalties   c) He made the shortest debut

7. How did Man Utd become known as the Red Devils?

   a) Sir Matt Busby chose it   b) A notorious spicy pie served in the 1950s at half time   c) A comment by a commentator

8. On the 1st March 1990 United lost 6 – 0 at Ipswich. What unusual feat did goalkeeper Gary Bailey achieve?

   a) He scored 2 own goals   b) He saved 3 penalties   c) He was sent off for hitting his own player

9. In 1956 the Busby Babes won the First Division title. What was their average age?

   a) 21   b) 22   c) 23

10. In the 1998 – 99 Champions League how many goals did United score against Bayern Munich?

    a) 2   b) 3   c) 5

11. Where did United buy Ray Wilkins from?

    a) Everton   b) Inter Milan   c) Chelsea

12. Who were the opponents when Andy Cole scored his first goal at Old Trafford?

    a) Newcastle   b) Man City   c) Man Utd

13. Who has played 129 times for their country scoring one goal?

    a) Peter Schmeichel   b) Jaap Stam   c) Denis Irwin

14. Who were the opponents when Eric Cantona executed his notorious kung fu kick?

    a) Arsenal   b) Crystal Palace   c) Man City

15. After winning the European Cup in 1968 United qualified for the Intercontinental Cup. Who did they play?

   a) Boca Juniors   b) Estudiantes   c) Racing Celtic

16. Which cricket club did Arnie Sidebottom play for?

   a) Middlesex   b) Yorkshire   c) Lancashire

17. Which goalkeeper scored against United in the 1967 Charity Shield?

   a) Gordon Banks   b) Pat Jennings   c) Peter Springett

18. Which club did United sign Lee Sharpe from?

   a) Torquay   b) Wycombe   c) Bury

19. In 1992 – 93 United were league champions. Which former manager oversaw the runners up?

   a) Tommy Docherty   b) Dave Sexton   c) Ron Atkinson

20. Who scored the first Premier League goal at Old Trafford?

   a) Peter Beardsley   b) Eric Cantona   c) Steve Bruce

21. In the 1998 – 99 Champions League final who scored the winning goal for United?

   a) Ole Solskjaer   b) Teddy Sheringham   c) Andy Cole

22. Where was Henning Berg signed from?

   a) Lillestrom b) Brondby   c) Blackburn

23. What was Joe Jordan's nickname?

   a) ET   b) Jaws   c) Jurassic

24. What nationality is Shinji Kagwa?

   a) South Korean   b) Vietnamese   c) Japanese

25. What nationality is Quinton Fortune?

   a) South African   b) American   c) Cameroonian

26. In 1994 – 95 United lost the title on the last day of the season to Blackburn after being held 1 – 1 by which team?

  a) Arsenal   b) Man City   c) West Ham

27. Pat McGibbon made his debut in a League Cup tie against York in September 1995 and United lost 3 – 0. Apart from all that why was it memorable for Pat?

  a) He was sent off   b) He fell over a photographer and was carried off c) He had two goals disallowed

28. United won the 1999 – 00 Premier League from Arsenal by how many points.

  a) 14 points   b) 16 points   c) 18 points

29. How many goals did they concede compared to Arsenal?

  a) 28 less   b) 24 less   c) 2 more

30. On the 28ᵗʰ August 2011 Man Utd won a Premier League game 8 – 2. Who were the opponents?

  a) Barnsley   b) Reading   c) Arsenal

31. Which club has Bobby Charlton, Nobby Stiles and Brian Kidd all managed?

  a) Preston North End   b) Bury   c) Blackpool

32. Which United player has played in Manchester, Merseyside and Old Firm derbies?

  a) Cleverley b) Kanchelskis   c) Fellaini

33. How many times have United done the League and FA Cup double?

  a) 1   b) 2   c) 3

34. What is the longest League streak without conceding a goal?

  a) 12   b) 14   c) 16

35. Ryan Giggs and Bobby Charlton are the two leading players by number of appearances for United. Who is third in the list?

　　a)　Bill Foulkes　　b) Paul Scholes　　c) Gary Neville

36. Who is the youngest player to have played for United?

　　a)　Mason Greenwood　　b) Norman Whiteside　　c) David Gaskell

37. Which goalkeeper has played the most games for United?

　　a)　Alex Stepney　　b) Harry Gregg　　c) Peter Schmeichel

38. Who has scored the fastest goal for United?

　　a)　George Best　　　b) Bryan Robson　　c) Denis Law

39. Who were United's first European opponents?

　　a)　Anderlecht　　b) Inter Milan　　c) Bayern Munich

40. What is the record home attendance for a Man Utd game?

　　a)　76,347　　　b) 81,235　　c) 83,260

41. Which United player has been sent off the most times in Premier League games?

　　a)　Roy Keane　　　b) Nicky Butt　　c) Paul Scholes

42. What nationality is Jesper Blomqvist?

　　a)　Icelandic　　b) Norwegian　　c) Swedish

43. How many times have United won the Premier League?

　　a)　11　　　b) 12　　c)13

44. Which Man Utd manager had the highest win %?

　　a)　Sir Alex Ferguson　　b) Jose Mourinho　　c) Sir Matt Busby

45. Who was known as the 'fifth Beatle'?

　　a)　Bobby Charlton　　b) Denis Law　　c) George Best

46. When was the last year that United didn't have a player who had come through their Academy in the team?

　　a)　1937　　　b) 1958　　　c) 2001

47. Who won the UEFA European Championship with his national team while playing for United?

    a) Ronaldo   b) Pogba   c) Schmeichel

48. United's first shirt sleeve sponsor was in 2018 and was Kohler. What do they do?

    a) Furniture   b) Plumbing goods   c) Electrical goods

49. Who has been the longest serving manager of United?

    a) Sir Alex Ferguson   b) Sir Matt Busby   c) Walter Crickmer

50. In 2008 United won the Champions League by beating Chelsea on penalties in the final. How many United players can you name who played in the game?

QUOTATIONS – WHO SAID IT?

1. As flies to wanton boys we are for the Gods.
2. 99% of players want to play for Manchester United and the rest are liars
3. Unlike humans dogs don't talk shit
4. I never comment on referees and I am not going to break the habit of a lifetime for that prat
5. Whichever team scores more goals usually wins
6. Maths is done totally differently to what I was teached when I was at school
7. After the match an official asked for two players to take a dope test. I offered the referee
8. Matt (Busby) was such an optimist he still hoped that Glenn Miller was just missing
9. I've never been involved with anyone who's set out to hurt people, to break legs. It's a bit of a dying art
10. Aggression is what I do. I go to war. You don't contest football matches in a reasonable state of mind

11. Football wasn't meant to be run by two linesmen and air traffic control
12. We had a virus that affected everyone at United. It was called winning
13. If there is a foul you have to fall. I call it 'helping the referee to make a decision'
14. If that was a penalty, I'll plait sawdust
15. Wayne Rooney has a man's body on a teenage head
16. No one wants to grow up to be Gary Neville
17. In 1969 I gave up women and alcohol. It was the worst twenty minutes of my life
18. I can't help but laugh at how perfect I am.
19. I once said Gazza's IQ was less than his shirt number and he asked me 'What's an IQ'
20. Before the game there was all this stuff about anti-racism and anti-bullying. It would be a good idea to start wearing wristbands for anti-diving
21. Gary Neville was captain and now Ryan Giggs has taken on the mantelpiece
22. That was in the past – we're in the future now
23. My best moment? I had a lot of good moments but the one I prefer is when I kicked the hooligan
24. I'm going to make a prediction. It could go either way
25. Nobby Stiles a dirty player? No, he never hurt anyone. Mind you, he's frightened a few.
26. Phil Neville was treading on dangerous water there
27. Your pace is deceptive son. You're even slower than you look
28. If a Frenchman goes on about seagulls, trawlers and sardines, he's called a philosopher. I'd just be called a short Scottish bum talking crap.
29. If we played like this every week we wouldn't be so inconsistent.
30. I don't mind Roy Keane making £60,000 a week. I was making the same when I was playing. The only difference was that I was printing my own.

31. People ask me what makes a great manager and I say it is good players. Crap players get you the sack, it's as simple as that.
32. You cannot lead by following
33. It wasn't going to be our day on the night
34. I don't play against a particular team. I play against the idea of losing
35. Every team has a hard man. We had Nobby Stiles, Chelsea had Chopper, Arsenal had Peter Storey, Liverpool had Tommy Smith. Leeds had eleven of them
36. They've kicked our backsides. We've got to lick our wounds...
37. I don't read papers, I don't gamble, I don't even know what day it is.
38. People say, 'go with the flow', but do you know what goes with the flow? Dead Fish
39. The rest of the Spice Girls wanted to invite the entire Bayern Munich team because they reckoned they'd never known blokes be on top for 90 minutes and still come second
40. In England they say Manchester is the city of rain. Its main attraction is considered to be the timetable at the railway station, where trains leave for other less rainy cities.
41. I would rather play with 10 men than wait for a player who is late for the bus
42. We are about creating a new wave of talent. We are the Manchester United of kitchens now.
43. Fergie said I was a Manchester United player in the wrong shirt. I said he was an Arsenal manager in the wrong blazer
44. Yes, I thought I was joining Manchester United, I was misled by all involved. I wasn't aware of another Manchester team.
45. If you want me to rule out being Manchester United manager, I can't. Special clubs need special managers, so in theory it could work.
46. And now International Soccer Special – Manchester United v Southampton

47. What do I think of the reverse sweep? It's like Manchester United getting a penalty and Bryan Robson taking it with his head

48. All I do know is that I will never be able to achieve what Tommy Docherty did, and that is take Aston Villa into the Third Division and Manchester United into the Second Division

49. Once you bid farewell to discipline you say goodbye to success

50. You'll never win anything with kids

Answers

QUIZ 1: THE START ANSWERS

1. 1878
2. Newton Heath LYR FC (LYR stands for Lancashire and Yorkshire Railway)
3. The colours were green and gold which were the companies of the railway company
4. It was the FA Cup in October 1886. The score finished 2 – 2 but Newton Heath were disqualified because they refused to play extra time.
5. It changed its name to Manchester United on the 24th April 1902
6. In 1933 – 34 United finished 20th in the Second Division and escaped relegation to the Third Division North by one point.
7. They enter the First Division in the 1892 – 93 season
8. They finished 20th and bottom. However due to a play off system they managed to retain their position in the First Division
9. Their first game at Old Trafford was on the 19th February 1910
10. It was against Liverpool and United lost 4 - 3

QUIZ 2: SIR ALEX FERGUSON ANSWERS

1. Chapman
2. East Stirlingshire
3. He won three
4. He was appointed 6th November 1986

5. He won the Premier League 13 times
6. Ron Atkinson
7. Oxford United
8. The score was 5 – 5
9. 2013
10. He won the FA Cup five times

QUIZ 3: SIR MATT BUSBY ANSWERS

1. Matt Busby was born on the 26th May 1909
2. Alexander
3. Collier
4. He signed for Man City on 11th February 1928 aged 18 and on £5 per week.
5. He played for Scotland once – a 3 - 2 defeat against Wales in 1933
6. He signed a contract on the 19th February 1945 and officially took over on 1st October 1945
7. He managed the Great Britain team at the 1948 London Olympics
8. He was offered the Real Madrid managers job
9. He won 5 titles – 1951 – 52, 1955 – 56, 1956 – 57, 1964 – 65 and 1966 – 67
10. A bit of a trick question. He won two as Man Utd manager – 1947 – 48 and 1962 – 62. However, he also won one playing for Man City in 1933 – 34. So, the answer is three.

Quiz 4: Jose Mourinho Answers

1. He was born in Portugal
2. Bobby Robson
3. He was appointed Benfica manager in September 2000
4. Van Gaal
5. He won three – EFL Cup 2016 – 17, FA Community Shield 2016 and the UEFA Europa League 2016 – 17
6. He has won the Champions League with Porto in 2003 – 04 and Inter Milan in 2009 – 10
7. Sevilla
8. They were second, nineteen points behind Man City
9. Chelsea won the final 1 - 0
10. Liverpool. They lost 3 – 1.

Quiz 5: David Moyes Answers

1. Glasgow
2. Celtic
3. Preston North End
4. Walter Smith
5. He was offered and signed a 6 year contract
6. 10 months
7. Community Shield 2013
8. Wigan
9. Man Utd were 7th
10. Real Sociedad

Quiz 6: Ole Solskjaer Answers

1. He was born on the 26th February 1973
2. He is Norwegian
3. He played 67 times for Norway and scored 23 goals
4. He was bought for £1.5m
5. He won 6 Premier League trophies – 1996 – 97, 1998 – 99, 1999 – 2000, 2000 – 01, 2002 – 03 and 2006 – 07
6. He scored 127 goals in 235 appearances
7. Molde
8. He signed for Cardiff
9. It was 19 games
10. They had won 14 of these games

Quiz 7: Louis van Gaal Answers

1. 8th August 1951
2. He was manager of Ajax from 1991 to 1997
3. They beat AC Milan 1 – 0
4. He took over from Bobby Robson
5. He won La Liga twice with Barcelona -1997 – 98 and 1998 – 99
6. They finished 3rd
7. He became manager on the 19th May 2014
8. It was LA Galaxy in a pre-season friendly which they won 7 – 0
9. They won the FA Cup defeating Crystal Palace 2 – 0
10. He was in charge for 103 games winning 54, drawing 25 and losing 24.

QUIZ 8: SIR BOBBY CHARLTON ANSWERS

1. He was born 11th October 1937
2. Jack Charlton
3. He made his debut against Charlton Athletic in October 1956
4. He was booked in the World Cup quarter final against Argentina on 23rd July 1966 for dissent
5. He scored 3. He scored one against Mexico in the group stage and two against Portugal in the semi-final
6. He played his last game against Chelsea on 28th April 1973
7. He made 758 appearances for Man Utd
8. He scored 249 times
9. He won three First Division titles – 1956 – 57, 1964 – 65 and 1966 - 67
10. He became manager of Preston NE in 1973

QUIZ 9: GEORGE BEST ANSWERS

1. Northern Ireland
2. He made his debut on the 14th September 1963
3. He made 470 appearances
4. He scored 179 goals
5. He was the leading goal scorer in 1967 – 68. He scored a total of 32 goals
6. Los Angeles Aztecs
7. He played for Fulham
8. He won it twice – 1964 - 65 and 1966 - 67
9. Hibernian
10. George Best sadly died on 25th November 2005

Quiz 10: Denis Law Answers

1. Huddersfield
2. He was bought from Torino
3. The fee was £115,000
4. He made 404 appearances
5. He scored a total of 237 goals
6. In the 1963 – 64 season he scored a total of 46 goals
7. The United Trinity
8. He holds the record with Kenny Dalglish
9. Dennis Bergkamp. The extra 'n' was put in to differentiate it from 'Denise'
10. He retired on the 26th August 1974

Quiz 11: Paul Pogba Answers

1. He was born in Lagny-sur-Marne and is French
2. Arsenal
3. His transfer from Le Havre was confirmed on the 7th October 2009 to join the Youth Academy
4. Man Utd got £0.8m for him. This was set by a tribunal
5. He won 4 – 2012 – 13, 2013 – 14, 2014 – 15 and 2015 - 16
6. The fee was £89.3m
7. Jose Mourinho
8. They beat Ajax 2 – 0. Pogba scored the opening goal.
9. He wears Adidas Predator boots
10. France won 4 - 2

QUIZ 12: BRYAN ROBSON ANSWERS

1. Chester-Le-Street on the 11th January 1957
2. West Brom
3. Ron Atkinson on 1st October 1981
4. He made 461 appearances
5. He scored a total of 99 goals for Man Utd
6. He won two Premier League titles in 1992 – 93 and 1993 - 94
7. He was appointed the Thailand manager on 23rd September 2009
8. He captained England 63 times
9. Middlesbrough in League Division One in 1994 – 95
10. He was an ambassador for Man Utd and worked alongside Bobby Charlton

QUIZ 13: ERIC CANTONA ANSWERS

1. He was born in Marseille on the 24th May 1966
2. It was a cave. His grandfather was a stonemason
3. Auxerre and made his debut on the 5th November 1983
4. He did National Service
5. The total fee was £1m, which consisted of £100k loan fee and £900k to sign him permanently
6. The last First Division title before the Premier League was formed
7. He played against Benfica in a friendly to mark Eusebio's 50th birthday
8. He won 4 titles – 1992 – 93, 1993 – 94, 1995 – 96 and 1996 – 97
9. He was 30 years old
10. He is an actor with over 25 film credits

Quiz 14: Old Trafford Answers

1. The first game was 19th February 1910
2. The game was against Liverpool and Liverpool won 4 – 3
3. The record attendance is 76,962 for an FA Cup semi final between Wolverhampton Wanderers and Grimsby Town on the 25th March 1939
4. The lowest attendance was between United and Fulham on the 29th April 1950 at 11,968
5. The Sir Alex Ferguson holds the most (21,401). The Sir Bobby Charlton Stand holds 9,433, the Stretford End 14,263 and the East Stand 13,307
6. Chris Eubank beat Nigel Benn in front of 42,000 spectators
7. Old Trafford is 105m x 68m
8. It was the Luftwaffe whose bombs hit the stadium several times. A raid on 11th March 1941 destroyed much of the stadium
9. They played at Maine Road paying £5,000pa rent while the stadium was rebuilt
10. The record win was against Ipswich on 4th March 1995. Andy Cole scored five goals

Quiz 15: 1960's Transfers Answers

1. Alex Stepney
2. He was signed from Arsenal and went on to play 202 games and scored 114 goals for United
3. Johnny Giles
4. He was bought from Burnley
5. Maurice Setters
6. Noel Cantwell
7. Dennis Violet

8. John Connelly for £56,000
9. Ian Ure
10. Harry Gregg

Quiz 16: 1970's Transfer Answers

1. Martin Buchan
2. Middlesbrough
3. Ted MacDougall who once scored 9 goals in a cup game for Bournemouth
4. He was signed from Arsenal
5. It was Hull
6. Steve Coppell was bought from Tranmere
7. It was Leeds Utd
8. Ray Wilkins
9. Joe Jordan
10. It was Arnie Sidebottom who played cricket for Yorkshire and played one Test match in 1980.

Quiz 17: 1980's Transfer Answers

1. They paid West Brom £1.5m for Bryan Robson
2. Paul McGrath
3. Frank Stapleton
4. Gordon Strachan
5. Norwich City
6. West Ham
7. It was Lee Sharpe
8. Inter Milan
9. It was Brian McClair who was signed from Celtic

10. He was sold to Everton

Quiz 18: 1990's Transfer Answers

1. He was signed from Oldham
2. He was signed from Brondby for £505,000
3. Dion Dublin
4. They paid £3.75m
5. It was Keith Gillespie
6. He arrived from Molde
7. He was signed from Spurs for £3.5m
8. They signed Jaap Stam
9. The player was Dwight Yorke
10. It was Gary Pallister who returned to Middlesbrough which was where he had been bought from.

Quiz 19: 2000's Transfer Answers

1. Fabien Barthez
2. He was 35 years old
3. Ruud van Nistelrooy
4. He arrived from Sporting CP
5. He left for Real Madrid
6. Rooney was 18 years old
7. He was signed on the 10th June 2005
8. Michael Carrick arrived from Spurs
9. He was signed on the 1st September 2008
10. He went to Bobby Robson's Newcastle

Quiz 20: 2010's Transfers Answers

1. He was bought from Fulham
2. The fee was £18.9m
3. He played 2 times under manager David Moyes
4. Robin van Persie scored 48 goals before moving to Fenerbahce
5. He went to Chinese Super League club Shandong Luneng
6. He scored 3 goals
7. Monaco
8. Sweden
9. Wayne Rooney
10. Ukraine

Quiz 21: First Division 1956 – 57 Answers

1. Spurs
2. Tommy Taylor scored 34 goals
3. They lost 2 – 1 to Aston Villa in the final
4. Ray Wood, the United goal keeper, was injured and had to leave the field. Jackie Blanchflower had to take over in goal as substitutes weren't allowed until 1965
5. Sir Matt Busby
6. Sir Bobby Charlton
7. They lost to Real Madrid 5 – 3 over the two legs
8. The largest gate was the away European Cup semi final against Real Madrid which was in front of 135,000 spectators. The Cup Final was in front of 100,000 and the Athletic Bilbao away leg was in front of 70,000
9. Old Trafford didn't have floodlights. The first match under floodlights was on the 25th March 1957 against Bolton in the First Division

10. It was Anderlecht with Dennis Violet getting 4 goals and Tommy Taylor 3 goals

QUIZ 22: FIRST DIVISION 1964 – 65 ANSWERS

1. It was Leeds United
2. The deciding factor was goal ratio. This was the number of goals scored divided by the number conceded. Manchester's ratio was 2.82 and Leeds' was 1.64. This system was scrapped in the 1976 – 77 season
3. Denis Law scored the most goals. His total was 28 goals in league and 39 in all competitions
4. It was Aston Villa with Denis Law getting 4 of them with David Herd 2 and John Connelly the other
5. It was Leeds United who won 1 – 0 after a 0 – 0 draw at Wembley
6. It was the Hungarian team Ferencvaros
7. Manchester had to host a trade fair
8. It was Harold Hardman who died a month after the season completed.
9. Bill Foulkes
10. Denis Law

QUIZ 23: EUROPEAN CHAMPIONS 1968 ANSWERS

1. The defending champions were Celtic, the 'Lions of Lisbon' beating Inter Milan in 1967
2. It was Eusebio who scored 6 goals in the competition
3. Benfica
4. Brian Kidd scored the other goal on his 19th birthday

5. They are a Maltese team
6. It was played at Wembley
7. Alex Stepney
8. Pat Crerand – Denis Law had a knee injury
9. AC Milan beat United 2 – 1 in the semi final
10. There were two players who has survived the disaster – Bobby Charlton and Bill Foulkes. In addition the manager, Matt Busby, was of course also a survivor.

QUIZ 24: FA CUP 1997 ANSWERS

1. It was Liverpool
2. 2 – 1
3. Jimmy Greenhoff scored 4 goals in the cup run
4. It was Leeds United
5. There was only one substitute
6. Martin Buchan
7. It was Tommy Docherty who was sacked less than 2 months after winning the Cup
8. Jimmy Greenhoff
9. Man Utd achieved the treble in 1998 – 99 season which was 22 seasons later
10. David McCreery

QUIZ 25: FA CUP WINNERS 1985 ANSWERS

1. Norman Whiteside
2. Everton
3. Kevin Moran
4. Ron Atkinson

5. It was Arthur Albiston
6. Olsen is from Denmark
7. They beat Liverpool in a replay
8. Paul McGrath
9. Norman Whiteside top scored with 4 goals in the 6 FA Cup games he played in
10. It was Bryan Robson

QUIZ 26: PREMIER LEAGUE 1992 -93 ANSWERS

1. It was 22 teams
2. Aston Villa
3. The first opponents were Sheffield United (A) and it didn't go well as Sheffield won 2 - 1
4. Mark Hughes scored 15 league goals
5. It was Umbro
6. The deal was for £305m
7. Ryan Giggs for the second year in succession
8. A bit of a trick question because it was Eric Cantona for Leeds United against Tottenham on the 25th August 1992. He signed for United on the 27th November 1992
9. Cambridge
10. It was Gary Pallister

QUIZ 27: THE TREBLE 1998 – 99 ANSWERS

1. Arsenal
2. The victims were Notts Forest with Solksjaer scoring 4 goals
3. Sharp
4. They beat Newcastle 2 – 0

5. Spurs beat them 3 -1 at White Hart Lane
6. It was Barcelona
7. They beat Juventus 4 – 3 on aggregate with a 3 – 2 win in Italy to clinch.
8. Dwight Yorke scored 29, Andy Cole 24 and Ole Solskjaer 18
9. Roy Keane
10. They didn't win any silverware in the season before the treble. In the League they lost a 12 point lead to Arsenal

Quiz 28: Premier League 2002 -03 Answers

1. Arsenal
2. Ruud van Nistelrooy was the League's leading scorer with 25 goals
3. It was Rio Ferdinand who was signed from Leeds United for £29.1m
4. It was Barthez
5. It was Vodafone
6. It was Roy Keane who is, of course, Irish
7. It was the last season for Man City at Maine Road before they moved to the City of Manchester Stadium
8. It was Diego Forlan who made a total of 18 sub appearances in the league
9. It was David Beckham who in the summer of 2003 left for Real Madrid
10. It was Newcastle and included a Paul Scholes hat trick

Quiz 29: European Cup Champions 2008 Answers

1. It was Chelsea. The score was 1 – 1 AET and United won 6 – 5 on penalties
2. The defending champions were AC Milan who were beaten 2 – 0 by Arsenal in the first knockout round
3. The game was played at the Luzhniki Stadium, Moscow
4. It was Frank Lampard
5. Ronaldo was the only one to miss a penalty for United
6. Ronaldo
7. United beat Barcelona 1 – 0 on aggregate
8. It was Ronaldo who scored 8 goals. Messi and Drogba got 6
9. Edwin van der Sar
10. There were 76 teams competing

Quiz 30: Premier League 2012 – 13 Answers

1. It was Barclays
2. Man City
3. Man City
4. The total is 20 titles with 7 being First Division and 13 Premier League titles
5. It was Robin van Persie who scored 26 league goals
6. Alex Ferguson was 71 when he retired
7. West Brom
8. The one missing out was Ryan Giggs
9. They lost 1 – 0 to Chelsea in a 6th round replay in the FA Cup, and 5 – 4 aet in the League Cup
10. Robin van Persie played in all 38 games, including coming off the bench three times

Quiz 31: FA Cup 2015 – 16 Answers

1. It was Crystal Palace
2. The 1990 final was between Man Utd and Crystal Palace and Man Utd won 1 – 0
3. The score was 2 – 1 to Man Utd
4. Jesse Lingard scored the winner in the 110th minute
5. It was Chris Smalling
6. United beat Everton 2 – 1
7. It was Romelu Lukaku
8. It was Louis van Gaal's only trophy, and he was sacked two days later
9. It is 12 wins
10. The player was Antonio Valencia

Quiz 32: Club Captains Answers

1. Ray Wilkins
2. Bryan Robson
3. Steve Bruce
4. Eric Cantona
5. Roy Keane
6. Gary Neville
7. Nemanja Vidic
8. Wayne Rooney
9. Michael Carrick
10. Antonio Valencia

Quiz 33: Sir Matt Busby Player of the Year Answers

1. Bryan Robson
2. Eric Cantona
3. David Beckham
4. Ryan Giggs
5. Teddy Sheringham
6. Ruud van Nistelrooy
7. Cristiano Ronaldo
8. Wayne Rooney
9. David de Gea
10. Luke Shaw

Quiz 34: Ruud van Nistelrooy Answers

1. PSV Eindhoven
2. It was fitness concerns. Man Utd wanted further medical tests and PSV refused. The day after the deal was cancelled Nistelrooy ruptured his anterior cruciate ligament in training.
3. He scored 25 goals in 32 games
4. He scored in 10 consecutive games. This was eventually broken by Jamie Vardy in 2015
5. He played in 150 Premier League games
6. He scored 95 goals in those games
7. He left for Real Madrid
8. He won it once in 2003 – 03
9. He achieved this 3 times – 2001 – 02, 2002 – 03 and 2003 – 04
10. He scored 150 goals in the five seasons in a total of 219 games

Quiz 35: Ryan Giggs Answers

1. He was born Ryan Wilson and changed his names to his mother's when his parents separated
2. He was at St David's Hospital, Cardiff
3. His father was Danny Wilson who played Rugby Union and Rugby League
4. He made his debut on 2nd March 1991 against Everton when he came on as a substitute
5. It was against Arsenal
6. He played 64 times for Wales
7. He has won the Premiership 13 times
8. He won the award in 2009
9. He played 963 games
10. He scored a total of 168 goals in those games

Quiz 36: Wayne Rooney Answers

1. Mark
2. He made his debut for Everton on the 17th August 2002 against Tottenham
3. Rooney has scored 253 goals in 553 appearances and Sir Bobby 249 in 758 appearances. So the answer is 4.
4. Macedonia
5. On 28th September he scored a hat trick against Fenerbahçe in a 6 – 2 win.
6. It is Michael Carrick
7. He scored 11 goals
8. DC United
9. He scored 25 goals
10. He joined Derby

Quiz 37: Bill Foulkes Answers

1. He joined the club in March 1950
2. He was a miner
3. He won 4 Championships – 1955 – 56, 1956 – 57, 1964 – 65 and 1966 - 67
4. He made 688 appearances
5. Foulkes only played once for England in 1954 against Northern Ireland
6. He retired on the 1st June 1970 aged 38
7. Wilf McGuinness
8. He scored 9 goals
9. He won one FA Cup in 1962 – 63
10. It went for £11,000

Quiz 38: Paul Scholes Answers

1. The Ammies
2. Oldham
3. He made his debut on the 21st September 1994 in the League Cup against Port Vale
4. On 24th September 1994 he played against Ipswich
5. He was booked in the Champions League 32 times. He was also booked 97 times in the Premier League
6. It was Didier Deschamps in the game against Juventus
7. It was in a 2 – 1 win against South Africa in 2007
8. He announced his first retirement, with immediate effect, on the 31st May 2011. This means he was 'retired' for 222 days
9. He won the title 11 times
10. He scored 155 goals for Man Utd

QUIZ 39: ROY KEANE ANSWERS

1. He is Roy Maurice Keane
2. He was born in Cork
3. Notts Forest
4. 1993
5. He received 11 red cards
6. It was Eric Cantona
7. He joined Celtic
8. He played 67 times and scored 9 times
9. Sunderland
10. Martin O'Neil

QUIZ 40: GARY NEVILLE ANSWERS

1. His name was Neville Neville
2. It was Matt Hayden
3. He made his debut in September 1992 against Torpedo Moscow in the UEFA cup
4. He scored a total of 5
5. He was appointed captain in November 2005 following Roy Keane's departure
6. Terry Venables
7. The correct answer could be said to be -2 as he didn't score any goals but did manage two own goals
8. It was Valencia
9. It was 8 titles
10. It was 602

Quiz 41: Mark Hughes Answers

1. He was born in Wrexham
2. Ron Atkinson
3. Barcelona where Terry Venables was manager
4. Bayern Munich
5. He scored 47 in his first spell and 116 goals in his second spell for a total of 163 goals
6. Chelsea
7. He received 14 yellow cards
8. On the 9th April 2002 he scored for Blackburn in a 2 – 1 win over Leicester
9. He was appointed the Welsh manager in 1999
10. He won two – 1992 – 93 and 1993 – 94 with Man Utd

Quiz 42: Alex Stepney Answers

1. He began at Millwall
2. He was acquired from Chelsea
3. United paid £55,000
4. He was born on the 18th September 1942
5. He has scored 2 goals. In 1973 – 74 he was the penalty taker.
6. He won one league title in 1966 – 67
7. He played 546 games for United
8. He joined the Dallas Tornado
9. Jimmy Case scored
10. Altrincham

Quiz 43: Duncan Edwards Answers

1. Dudley
2. Surprisingly it was Morris Dancing
3. Carpenter
4. 16 years 185 days
5. He played 151 times for United
6. He was paid £15 per week during the season and £12 during the summer
7. He won the league twice – 1955 - 56 and 1956 – 57
8. 18
9. It was Arsenal and the game finished 5 – 4 to United with Edwards scoring the opening goal
10. He was fined two weeks wages

Quiz 44: Premier League Winners 1995 – 96

Answers

1. Newcastle
2. They beat Liverpool 1 – 0
3. They lost 4 – 3 to York City on aggregate
4. Eric Cantona was the leading league scorer with 14 goals
5. It was Man City
6. Gary Neville
7. They beat Bolton 6 – 0 on the 25th February 1996
8. It was Sharp
9. Peter Schmeichel
10. Middlesbrough

Quiz 45: First Division Winners 1951 – 52 Answers

1. It was 41 years since they last won the First Division in the 1910 – 11 season.
2. Tottenham
3. It was John Aston Sr. John Aston Jr played for United from 1965 – 72
4. Johnny Carey
5. Sir Matt Busby
6. Jack Rowley who scored 30 goals in 40 games
7. It was Arsenal
8. Johnny Carey
9. Johnny Berry. He played 247 games for United and retired due to injuries sustained in the Munich Plane Crash
10. Allenby Chilton played every game. He missed just 13 games in 9 seasons at United

Quiz 46: Europa League Winners 2016 – 17 Answers

1. The final was held at Friends Arena in Solna, which is a suburb of Stockholm
2. Ajax
3. United won 2 – 0
4. It was the Special One – Jose Mourinho
5. Ander Herrera
6. They beat Celta Vigo 2 – 1 on aggregate
7. Henrikh Mkhitaryan scored 6 goals
8. They lost to Chelsea in the quarter- finals of the FA Cup
9. Antonio Valencia was captain
10. Fenerbahçe finished top by one point over United. Both went through to the knockout stage

Quiz 47: 2ND Division Champions 1974 – 75 Answers

1. They had been champions once before in the 1937 – 38 season
2. It was Tommy Docherty
3. Aston Villa finished second and were 3 points behind United
4. It was Stuart Pearson who scored 17 goals in 31 games in 1974 – 75.
5. Pearson was signed from Hull in May 1974
6. Derby won the First Division Championship
7. Paddy Roche
8. It was Willie Morgan
9. Norwich beat United 3 – 2 on aggregate over two legs
10. The average home gate this season was 47,781 so 48,000 is the answer

Quiz 48: FA Cup 1990 Answers

1. They beat Crystal Place 1 – 0 after a 3 - 3 draw in the first final.
2. Lee Martin
3. They beat Oldham 2 – 1 in a replay after drawing 3 - 3 in the first game
4. He replaced goalkeeper Jim Leighton with Les Sealey in the final replay
5. The song was 'We will stand together'
6. Ian Wright scored two goals in the first game
7. It was Sir Alex's first trophy with United so he had won nothing prior to this for Man Utd.
8. They finished thirteenth
9. Mark Hughes was top scorer with 15 goals in the season
10. They didn't have any home games. The only time this has happened to a winner of the competition

Quiz 49: Charity/Community Shield

1. United beat Leicester 2 - 1
2. United beat Wigan 2 - 0
3. United beat Man City 3 - 2
4. United beat Chelsea 3 - 1
5. United beat West Ham 3 - 1 on penalties after no score after 90 minutes
6. United beat Chelsea 3 – 0 on penalties after being 1 - 1 after 90 minutes
7. United beat Arsenal 4 – 3 on penalties after drawing 1 – 1 after 90 minutes
8. United beat Chelsea 4 – 2 on penalties after being 1 – 1 after 90 minutes
9. United beat Newcastle 4 - 0
10. United beat Blackburn 2 - 0

Quiz: 50 Miscellaneous Answers

1. During the 1987-88 season Man Utd had a tour of Bermuda and played two matches. Sir Alex played in the second game against Somerset Cricket Club.
2. Denis Law won it in the 1964 - 65 season.
3. 1994
4. Viv Anderson who was bought from Arsenal
5. Denis Law playing for Man City
6. It was the shortest debut in Premier League history.
   Nick Culkin replaced Raimond van der Gouw who was injured in stoppage time. Culkin took the resulting free kick and the referee immediately blew for full time.

7. Sir Matt chose it as it was decided they should move on from the 'Busby Babes' following the Munich Crash. It was based on Salford Rugby Club's French tour of the 1930s
8. He saved three penalties
9. The average age was 21
10. United played Bayern in the Group Stage so the answer is 5. The scores were 2 – 2 and 1 - 1 in the group stage and 2 - 1 in the final.
11. Chelsea
12. It was Man Utd. He scored for Newcastle
13. Peter Schmeichel
14. It was Crystal Palace in January 1995
15. Estudiantes
16. It was Yorkshire with whom he got an England cricket cap
17. Pat Jennings
18. Torquay in June 1988
19. It was Ron Atkinson who was manager of Aston Villa
20. Peter Beardsley scored in a 3 – 0 defeat to Everton
21. Ole Solskjaer
22. Blackburn
23. Jaws due to the absence of front teeth
24. Japanese
25. South African
26. West Ham
27. He was sent off and never played for United again
28. United's lead over Arsenal was 18 points
29. They conceded 45 goals which was two more than Arsenal
30. Arsenal
31. Preston North End
32. Andrei Kanchelskis
33. They have done it 3 times – 1993 – 94, 1995 – 96 and 1998 – 99
34. They went 14 games without conceding from 15th November 2008 to 18th February 2009
35. Paul Scholes who made 718 appearances

36. David Gaskell. He played in the 1956 Charity Shield at the age of 16 years and 19 days
37. Alex Stepney who made 539 appearances
38. Bryan Robson scored in 12 seconds on the 26th September 1984 against Burnley in a League Cup game
39. Anderlecht on 12 September 1956 which United won 2 – 0
40. 83,260 saw Man Utd play Arsenal on 17th January 1948. The game was played at Maine Road while repairs were carried out at Old Trafford
41. Roy Keane who was sent off 7 times for United
42. He is Swedish
43. They have won it 13 times – 1992 – 93, 1993 – 94, 1995 – 96, 1996 – 97, 1998 – 99, 1999 – 00, 2000 – 01, 2002 – 03, 2006 – 07, 2007 – 08, 2008 – 09, 2010 – 11 and 2012 – 13
44. Sir Alex Ferguson has 59.67% wins, Jose Mourinho 58.33% wins and Sir Matt Busby has 50.48% wins
45. George Best
46. It was the 30th October 1937. That is now over 4,000 consecutive matches
47. It was Peter Schmeichel who won the competition with Denmark in 1992
48. Plumbing goods
49. It is Sir Alex Ferguson who was manager for 26 years 194 days and covered 1500 matches
50. Edwin van der Sar, Wes Brown, Rio Ferdinand, Nemanja Vidic, Patrice Evra, Owen Hargreaves, Paul Scholes, Michael Carrick, Cristiano Ronaldo, Wayne Rooney, Carlos Tevez, Anderson, Ryan Giggs and Nani

QUOTATIONS ANSWERS

1. Eric Cantona
2. Gordon McQueen
3. Roy Keane
4. Ron Atkinson
5. Michael Owen
6. David Beckham
7. Tommy Docherty
8. Pat Crerand
9. Steve Bruce
10. Roy Keane
11. Tommy Docherty
12. Sir Alex Ferguson
13. Jose Mourinho
14. Ron Atkinson
15. George Graham
16. Jaimie Carragher
17. George Best
18. Zlatan
19. George Best
20. Roy Keane
21. Rio Ferdinand
22. David Beckham
23. Eric Cantona
24. Ron Atkinson
25. Sir Matt Busby
26. Ron Atkinson
27. Tommy Docherty to Leighton James
28. Gordon Strachan
29. Bryan Robson
30. Mickey Thomas
31. Tommy Docherty
32. Sir Alex Ferguson
33. Bryan Robson

34. Eric Cantona
35. George Best
36. Steve Bruce
37. Steve McClaren
38. Roy Keane
39. Gary Neville
40. Nemanja Vidic
41. Jose Mourinho
42. Gordon Ramsey
43. Tony Adams
44. Robinho
45. Jose Mourinho
46. David Coleman
47. David Lloyd
48. Ron Atkinson
49. Sir Alex Ferguson
50. Alan Hansen

ONE LAST THING...

If you have enjoyed this book I would love you to write a review of the book on Amazon. It is really useful feedback as well as giving untold encouragement to the author.

If you have any comments, corrections, suggestions for improvements or for other books I would love to hear from you, and you can contact me at;
m.prefontaine2@gmail.com

Your comments are greatly valued, and the books have already been revised and improved as a result of helpful suggestions from readers.

Printed in Great Britain
by Amazon